Success

Assessment Papers

Maths

8 – 9 years · levels 3 – 4

Paul Broadbent

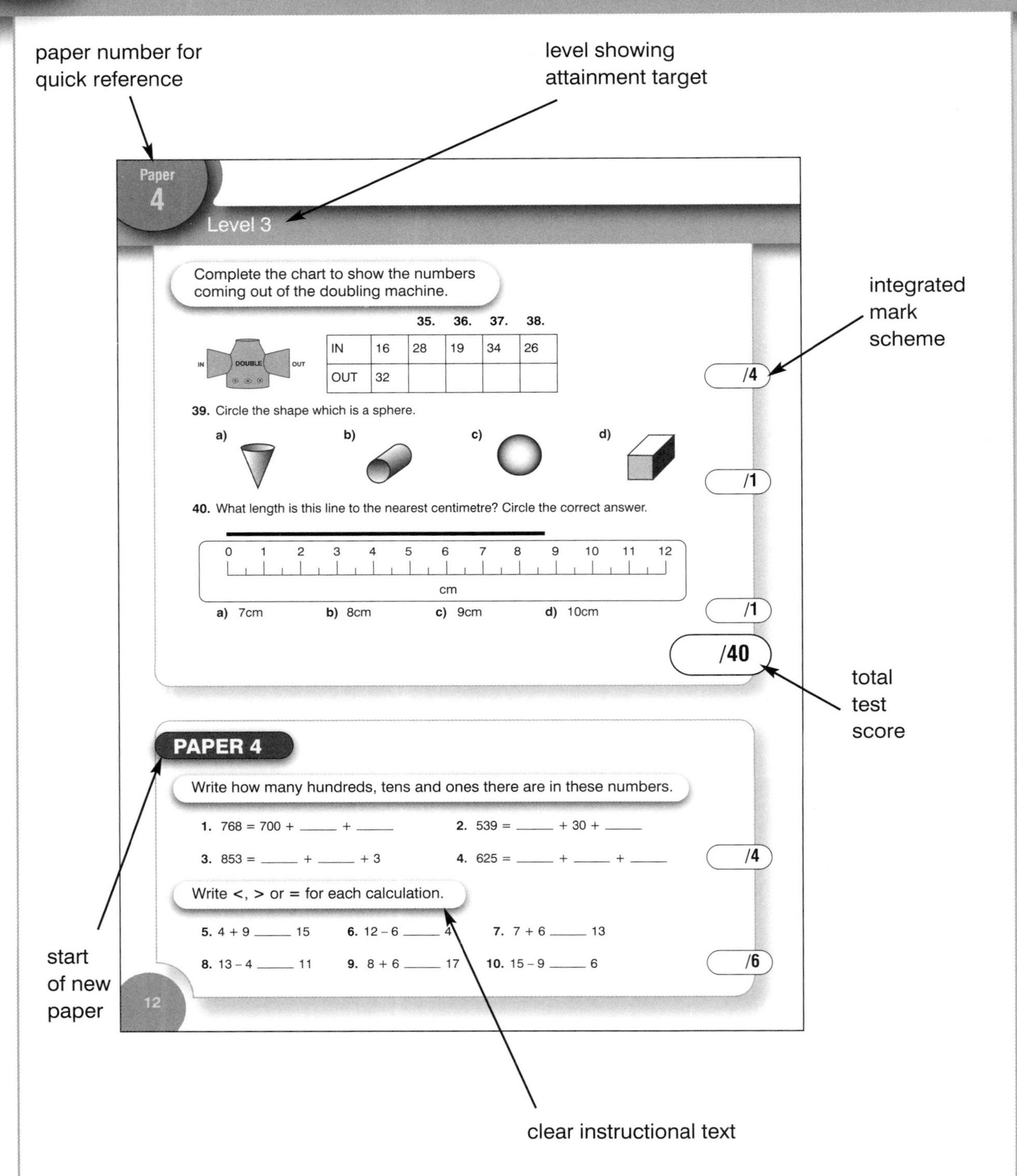

Paper 4

Level 3

Complete the chart to show the numbers coming out of the doubling machine.

		35.	36.	37.	38.
IN	16	28	19	34	26
OUT	32				

/4

39. Circle the shape which is a sphere.

a) **b)** **c)** **d)**

/1

40. What length is this line to the nearest centimetre? Circle the correct answer.

0 1 2 3 4 5 6 7 8 9 10 11 12

cm

a) 7cm **b)** 8cm **c)** 9cm **d)** 10cm

/1

/40

PAPER 4

Write how many hundreds, tens and ones there are in these numbers.

1. 768 = 700 + _____ + _____

2. 539 = _____ + 30 + _____

3. 853 = _____ + _____ + 3

4. 625 = _____ + _____ + _____

/4

Write <, > or = for each calculation.

5. 4 + 9 _____ 15

6. 12 – 6 _____ 4

7. 7 + 6 _____ 13

8. 13 – 4 _____ 11

9. 8 + 6 _____ 17

10. 15 – 9 _____ 6

/6

12

Contents

PAPER 1

1. What is the missing number? [16] ÷ 4 = 4

a) 8 **b)** 1 **c)** 16 **d)** 12

/1

2. Which number is the arrow pointing to? [115]

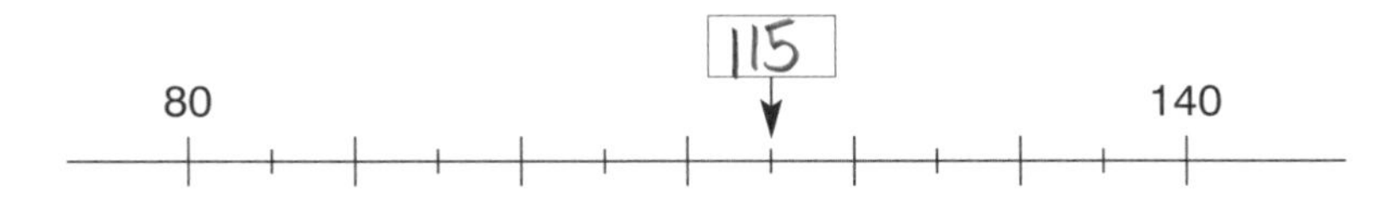

/1

Write in the missing numbers or words.

3. 971 → nine hundred and ~~one~~ seventy one

4. 426 → four hundred and twenty-six

5. 526 → 5 hundred and 20 6

6. 219 → two hundred and nineteen

/4

What are the next two numbers in each sequence?

7. 22 27 32 37 42 47 52

8. 85 87 89 91 93 95 97

9. 61 64 67 70 73 76 79

10. 44 48 52 56 60 64 68

/4

Write the missing numbers.

11. 6 + [9] = 15 **12.** 13 − [8] = 5 **13.** [18] − 9 = 9 **14.** [4] + 8 = 12

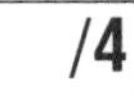
/4

15. What is the area of this rectangle? Circle the correct answer.

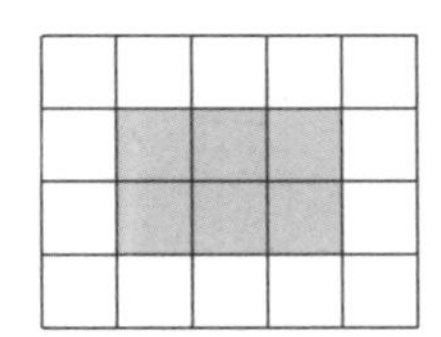

a) 6 squares

b) 5 squares

c) 9 squares

d) 8 squares

/1

13 − 12 = 1

0 − 9 = −9

Name the shapes in each set and cross out the odd one out.

sphere cuboid prism cylinder cone cube

16.

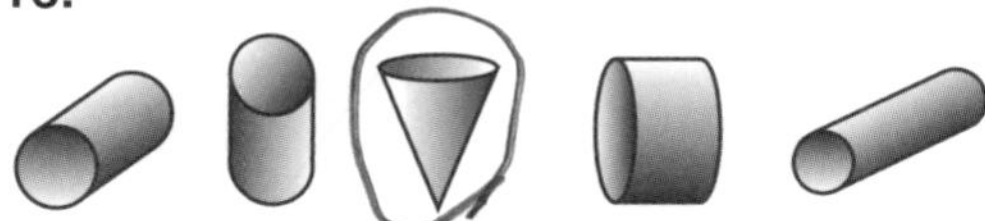

These shapes are all cylinder.

The odd one out is a cone.

17.

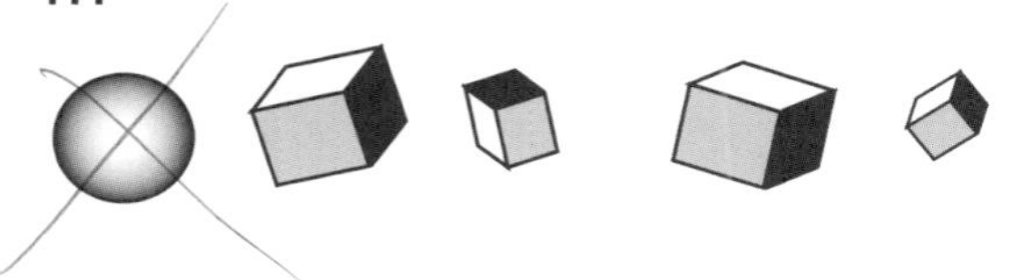

These shapes are all cube.

The odd one out is a sphere.

18.

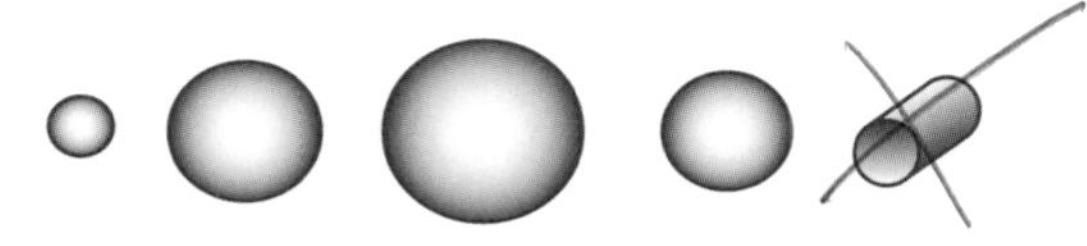

These shapes are all Sphere.

The odd one out is a Cylinder.

19.

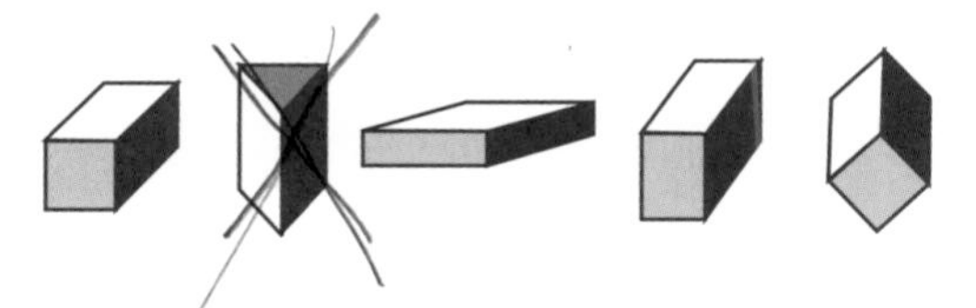

These shapes are all cuboid.

The odd one out is a prism.

/4

Answer these.

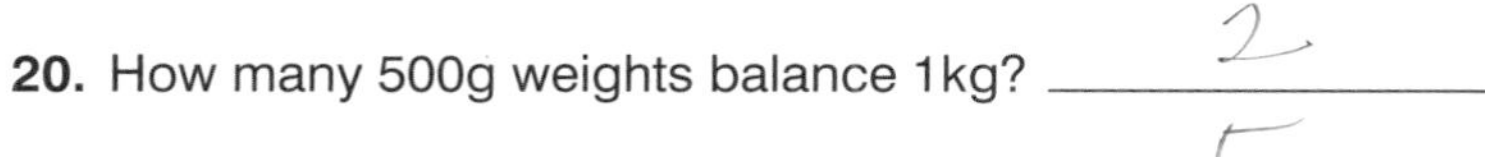

20. How many 500g weights balance 1kg? 2

21. How many 200g weights balance 1kg? 5

22. How many 100g weights balance 1kg? 10

23. How many 50g weights balance 1kg? 20

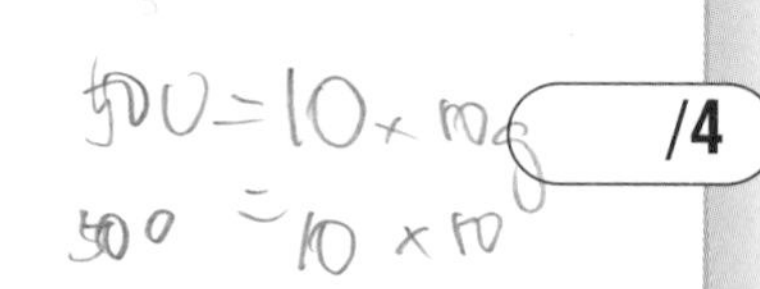

/4

Write the fraction of the part shaded on each flag.

24. $\frac{1}{4}$ 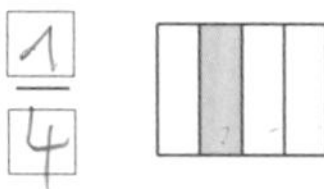

25. $\frac{1}{3}$

26. $\frac{1}{6}$ 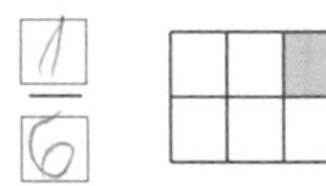

27. $\frac{1}{8}$ 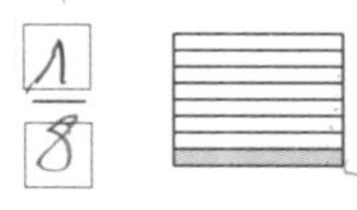

28. $\frac{1}{5}$ 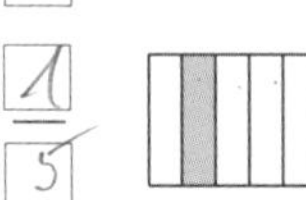

29. $\frac{1}{9}$ 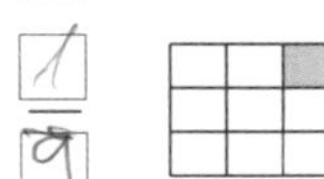

/6

Use a ruler to measure the exact length of each line.

30. length: 6 cm

31. length: 8 cm

32. length: 5 cm

/3

Answer these.

33. How many days in 4 weeks? 28

34. How many wheels on 8 bicycles? 16

35. How many shoes in 5 pairs? 10

36. There are 4 legs on a table. How many legs are needed to build 4 tables? 16

37. There are 6 eggs in a box, how many eggs in 5 boxes? 30

/5

What times are shown on these clocks?

38.

6:15

39.

3:45

40.

5:30

/3

/40

PAPER 2

1. Circle the missing number. 463 = ☐ + 60 + 3

a) 4 **b)** 400 **c)** 40 **d)** 4000

/1

Write the numbers shown on each abacus.

2. 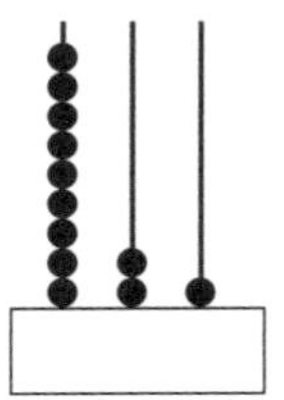

3. 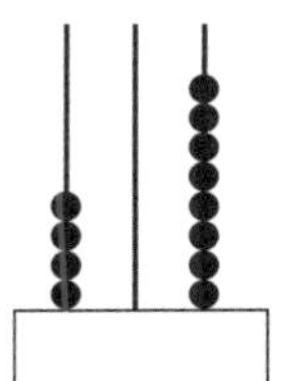

4. 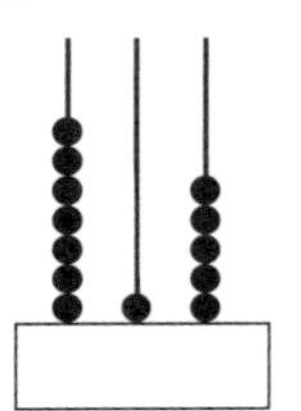

5. 

/4

Draw one line of symmetry on each shape.

6. 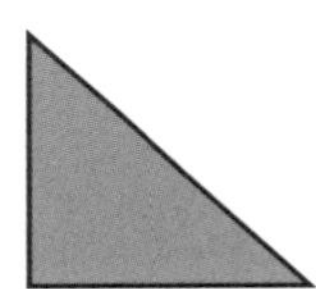

7. 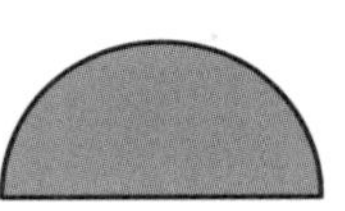

8. 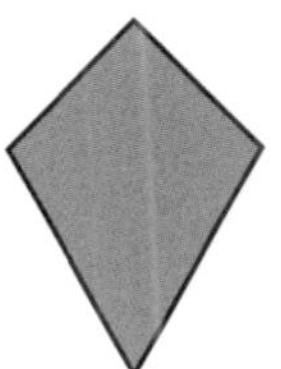

/3

9. How much water is in this jug?

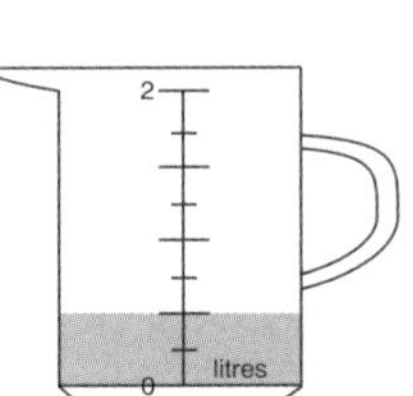

__________ ml

/1

Complete these.

10. 20 ÷ 5 = __________

11. 18 ÷ 3 = __________

12. 24 ÷ 4 = __________

13. 35 ÷ 5 = __________

/4

14. Which clock shows 6.45? Circle the correct answer.

a) 

b) 

c) 

d) 

/1

Complete these.

15. 2000g = ________ kg

16. 5kg = ________ g

17. 4000ml = ________ l

18. 6 l = ________ ml

/4

19. What is the approximate area of this shape?
Circle the correct answer.

a) 8 squares **b)** 7 squares

c) 6 squares **c)** 5 squares

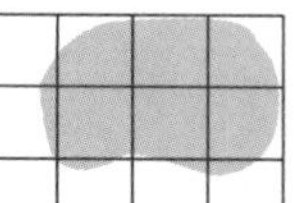

/1

Write the next two numbers in each sequence.

20. 100 96 92 88 84 __ __

21. 38 33 28 23 18 __ __

22. 73 71 69 67 65 __ __

23. 55 52 49 46 43 __ __

/4

Complete this chart.

Name of shape	Total number of faces	Number of square faces	Number of rectangle faces	Number of triangular faces
24. Cube				
25. Cuboid				
26. Triangular prism				

/3

Write the missing numbers.

27. $40 + \square = 100$

28. $\square - 200 = 700$

29. $80 - \square = 30$

30. $\square + 400 = 600$

/4

Read and answer these.

My mother is 36 . . .

31. My aunt is 3 years older than my mother. How old is my aunt? ________

32. My grandfather is 30 years older than my mother. How old is my grandfather? ________

33. My father is 5 years older than my aunt. How old is my father? ________

34. My uncle is 4 years older than my father. How old is my uncle? ________

35. My grandmother was 20 when my mother was born. How old is my grandmother? ________

36. My great-grandmother is 50 years older than my mother.
How old is my great-grandmother? ________

/6

37. Circle the correct fraction.

a) $\frac{1}{2}$ b) $\frac{1}{5}$

c) $\frac{1}{6}$ d) $\frac{1}{3}$

0 1

/1

Answer these.

38. I'm thinking of a number. If I divide it by 3, the answer is 15. What is my number? ________

39. I'm thinking of a number. If I multiply it by 4, the answer is 24. What is my number? ________

40. I'm thinking of a number. If I divide it by 5, the answer is 10. What is my number? ________

/3

/40

PAPER 3

Write how many 100s, 10s and 1s there are in each of these numbers.

1. 398 = 300 + ☐ + ☐ **2.** 217 = ☐ + 10 + ☐

3. 452 = ☐ + ☐ + 2 **4.** 683 = ☐ + ☐ + ☐

5. 165 = ☐ + ☐ + ☐ **6.** 709 = ☐ + ☐ + ☐

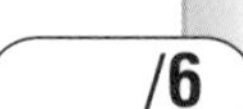

Write in the missing < or > signs for each pair of numbers.

7. 64 ☐ 54 **8.** 28 ☐ 31 **9.** 90 ☐ 19 **10.** 36 ☐ 23

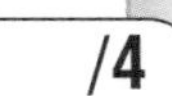

11. Which of these is a symmetrical shape? Circle the correct answer.

a) 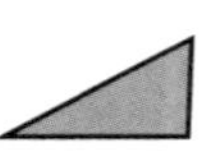 **b)** 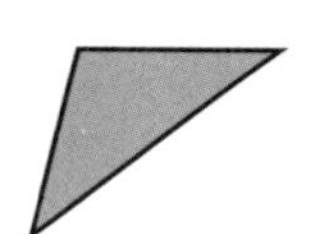 **c)** 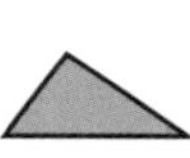 **d)** 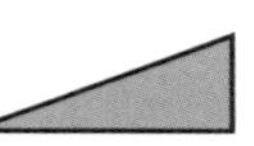

/1

12. What is the weight of this parcel?

_________ kg

Answer these.

13. A cup holds $\frac{1}{2}$ litre of water. A pot holds 4 litres. How many cupfuls will fill the pot? _________

14. A bucket holds 8 litres of water.
It is poured out equally into 4 jugs. How much water is in each jug? _________

15. A jug holds $2\frac{1}{2}$ litres of juice and a bottle
holds 4 litres of juice. How much more juice is in the bottle? _________

16. Three jugs each hold $1\frac{1}{2}$ litres of water.
The water is poured into a 4 litre bucket.
Some water is left in one of the jugs. How much water is left in the jug? _________

/4

17. Marvin has a box of stamps. He puts them in groups of 3 and has 1 left over.
He puts them in groups of 4 and still has 1 left over.
He has less than 20 stamps. How many stamps has he got? ________ /1

Answer these problems.

18. A cartoon started at 3.15 and lasted for 30 minutes. At what time did it finish? ________

19. Alice got on a bus at 11.45. The journey took half an hour.
What time did she get off the bus? ________

20. A pie needs to be in the oven for 1 hour 30 minutes. If it needs to be taken out of the oven at 6.30, what time should it be put in the oven? ________

21. Sam went to football at 5.30. He was there until 7.00.
How long was he at football? ________ /4

Write each group of numbers in order starting with the smallest.

22. 59	91	12	25	________
23. 73	87	78	83	________
24. 45	68	22	39	________
25. 61	16	60	10	________

/4

Use each of the numbers 5, 6, 7, 8, 9 and 10 to fill in the six missing numbers.

26. $\square + \square = 15$ 27. $\square + \square > 15$ 28. $\square + \square < 15$ /3

Write the difference between each pair of numbers.

29. 98 30 ________ 30. 50 57 ________

31. 30 76 ________ 32. 82 40 ________

33. 20 44 ________ 34. 50 91 ________ /6

Complete the chart to show the numbers coming out of the doubling machine.

		35.	36.	37.	38.
IN	16	28	19	34	26
OUT	32				

/4

39. Circle the shape which is a sphere.

a) 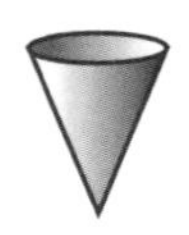

b) 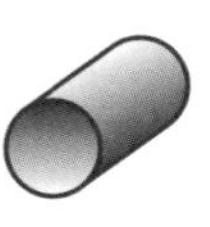

c) 

d) 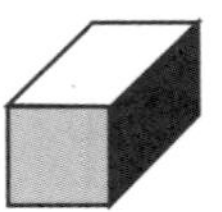

/1

40. What length is this line to the nearest centimetre? Circle the correct answer.

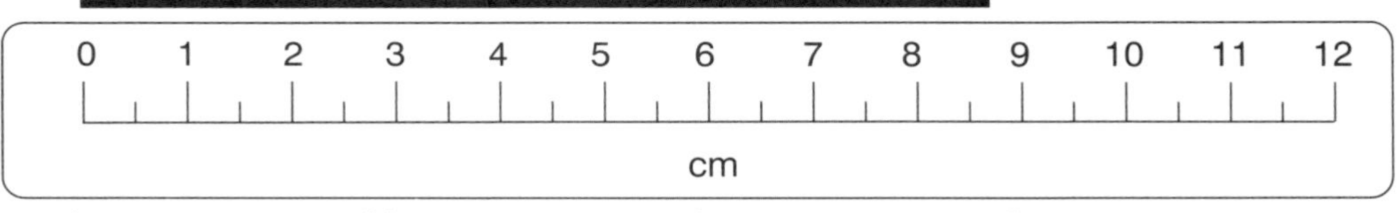

a) 7cm **b)** 8cm **c)** 9cm **d)** 10cm

/1

/40

PAPER 4

Write how many hundreds, tens and ones there are in these numbers.

1. 768 = 700 + ______ + ______

2. 539 = ______ + 30 + ______

3. 853 = ______ + ______ + 3

4. 625 = ______ + ______ + ______

Write <, > or = for each calculation.

5. 4 + 9 ______ 15

6. 12 – 6 ______ 4

7. 7 + 6 ______ 13

8. 13 – 4 ______ 11

9. 8 + 6 ______ 17

10. 15 – 9 ______ 6

/6

11. What is the total area of this shape? Circle the correct answer.

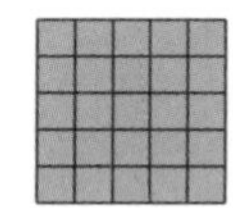

a) 5 squares **b)** 20 squares

c) 25 squares **d)** 10 squares

/1

12. These shapes weigh 22kg altogether. If each sphere weighs 6kg, what is the weight of each cube?

Cube = ____________kg

/1

13. Which clock shows 8.45? Circle the correct answer.

a) 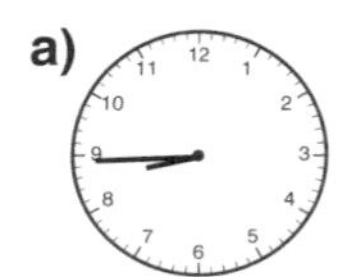

b) 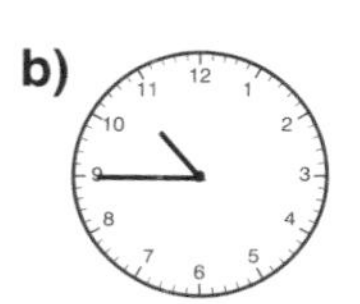

c) 

d) 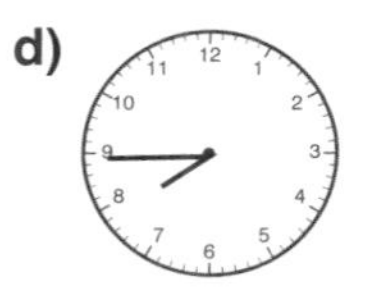

/1

14. Use the digits 0 to 5.  0 1 2 3 4 5

☐ x ☐ = 12 ☐ x 5 = ☐ 0 ☐ x 8 = 4 ☐

/1

Write the numbers shown on each abacus.

15. 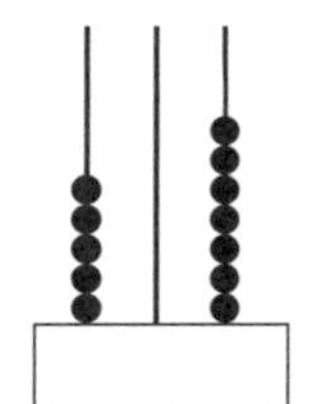

16. 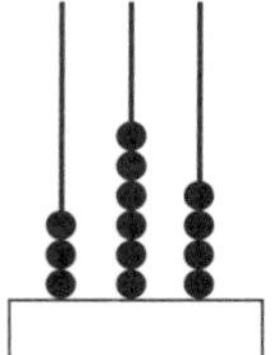

17. 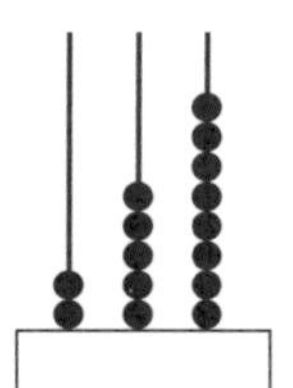

18. 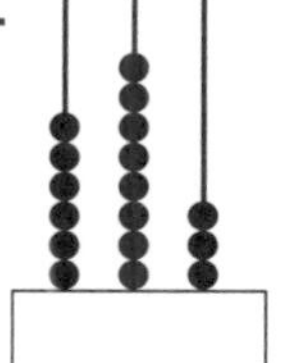

/4

Write the missing numbers in each sequence.

19.	27	☐	47	☐	67	77
20.	15	19	☐	27	31	☐
21.	41	46	☐	☐	61	66
22.	☐	92	88	82	☐	72
23.	96	☐	92	90	☐	86
24.	☐	29	32	35	38	☐

/6

Name these shapes.

25.  ____________

26. ____________

27.  ____________

28. ____________

29. ____________

Write the fraction shown by each arrow on these number lines.

30. 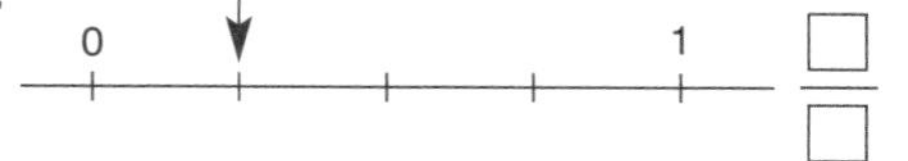

31. 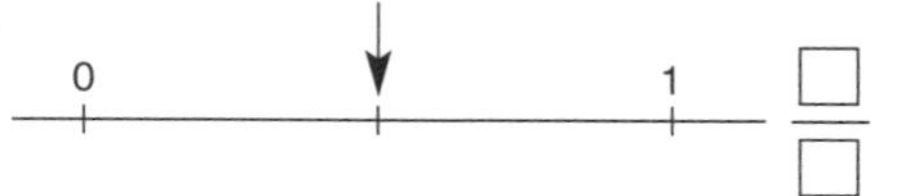

32. 

33. 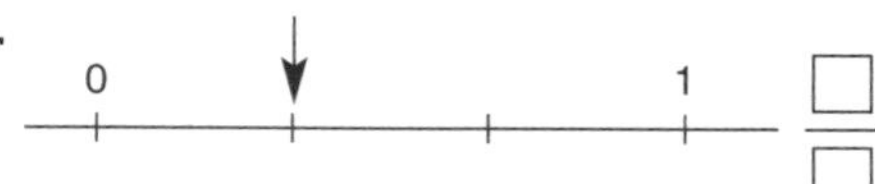

34. 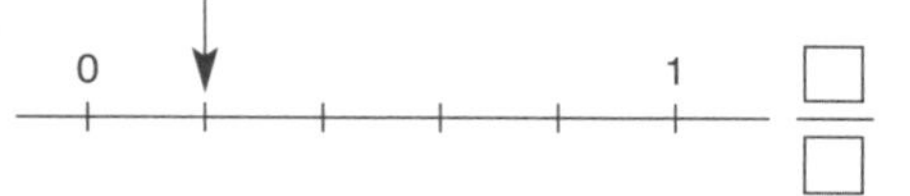

/5

35. How many faces has a cuboid got? Circle the correct answer.

a) 8 **b)** 6 **c)** 12 **d)** 4

/1

36. I'm thinking of a number.
If I multiply it by 2, the answer is 14. What is my number? ____________

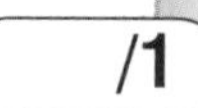

37. Complete this multiplication grid.

X	7	3	9
5			45
4	28		

/1

Answer these.

38. $32 \div 8 =$ ________ 39. $45 \div 9 =$ ________ 40. $27 \div 3 =$ ________

/40

PAPER 5

Write the numbers that went into these number machines.

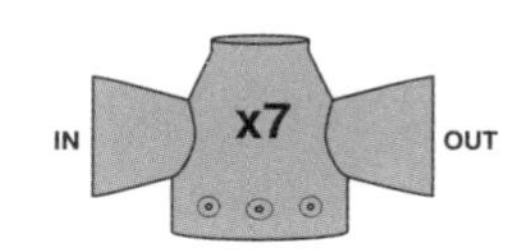

	1.	2.	3.	4.	5.
IN					
OUT	70	63	35	14	28

/5

Complete these.

6. 7000g = ______ kg

7. 8 litres = ______ ml

8. 300cm = ______m

9. 6000m = ______ km

/4

10. Which number could be missing? Circle the correct answer. 374 > ☐ > 298

a) 381 **b)** 294 **c)** 301 **d)** 270

/1

11. There are some birds' nests in a large tree. Two of the nests have 5 eggs in them. The other nests have 3 eggs in them. There are 25 eggs altogether.

How many nests have 3 eggs in them? ______________

12. What is the weight of this parcel?

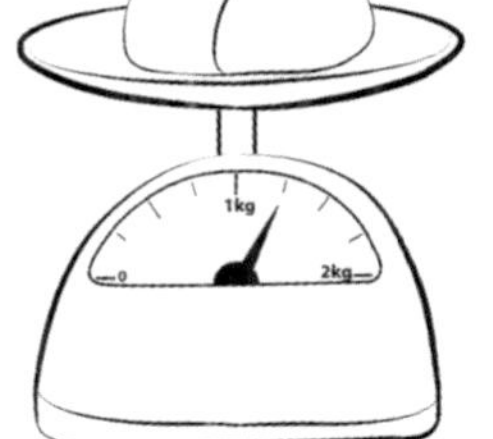

___ kg _____ g

/2

What are the halfway numbers on these number lines?

13.

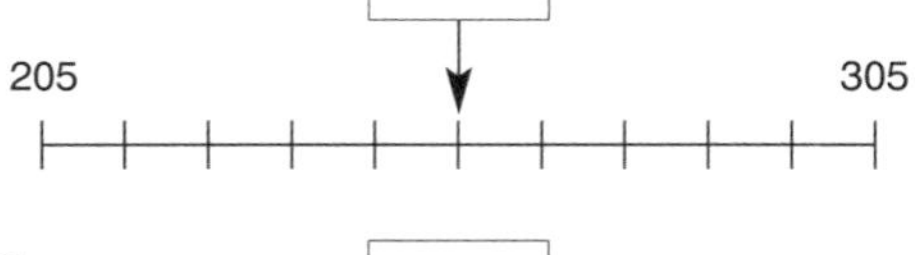

14.

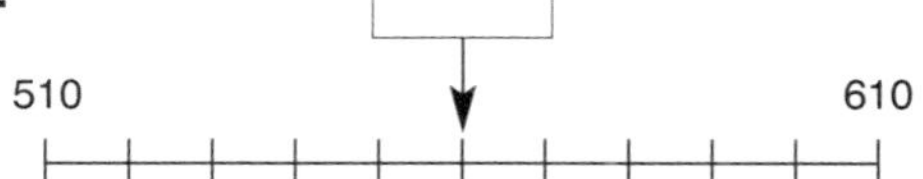

15.

/3

Read and answer these.

16. What is the sum of 50 and 40? ______________

17. What is the total of 6 and 18? ______________

18. What is the difference between 14 and 7? ______________

19. Which number is 300 less than 900? ______________

20. What is 200 more than 500? ______________

/5

Write the name of the shapes in each set. Cross out the odd one out.

21. 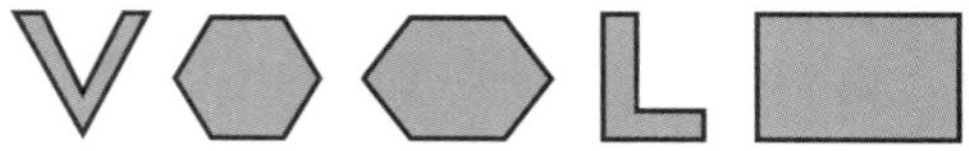 These shapes are all ________________.

The odd one out is a ________________.

22.  These shapes are all ________________.

The odd one out is a ________________.

23. 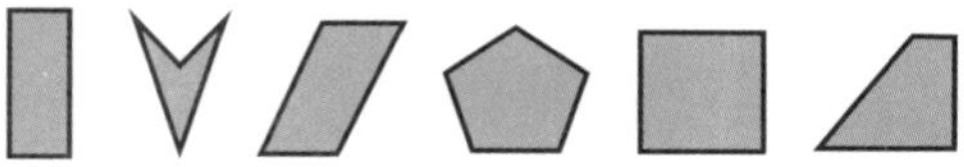 These shapes are all ________________.

The odd one out is a ________________.

24. 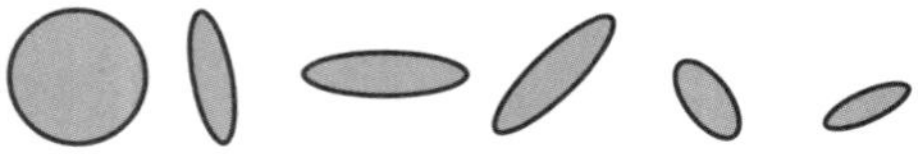 These shapes are all ________________.

The odd one out is a ________________.

/4

Use a ruler to measure the exact length of each line.

Write each length in centimetres.

25. length: ______cm

26. length: ______cm

27. length: ______cm

/3

Read and answer these.

28. A baker sells 6 doughnuts in a bag.
How many bags can be filled with 18 doughnuts? ________

29. There are 16 socks that are put into 2s.
How many pairs of socks are there? ________

30. A farmer has 40 tomato plants and puts 5
in each row. How many rows will there be? ________

/3

Answer these.

31. How many minutes in one hour? ____________

32. How many days in one week? ____________

33. How many months in a year? ____________

34. Which day comes after Wednesday? ____________

35. Which day comes before Sunday? ____________

36. Which month comes after March? ____________

/6

What is the approximate area of these shapes?

37.

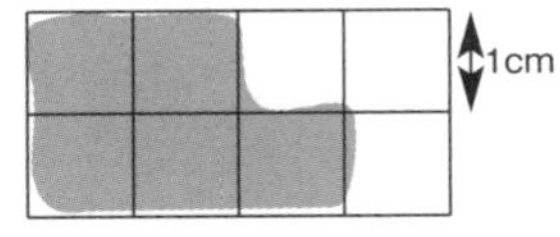

Area = approximately _____ cm^2

38.

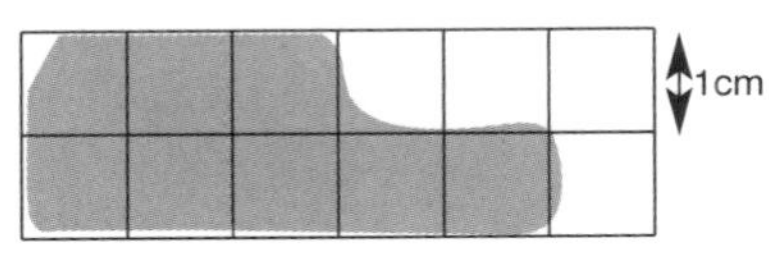

Area = approximately _____ cm^2

39.

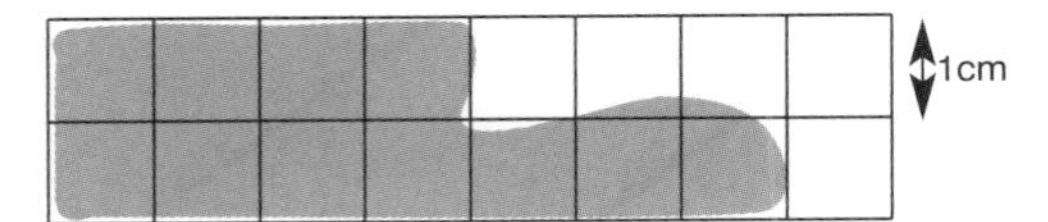

Area = approximately _____ cm^2

/3

40. Which of these has a curved face? Circle the correct answer.

a) cube **b)** cylinder **c)** prism **d)** pyramid

/1

/40

PAPER 6

1. These shapes weigh 8kg altogether.
If each sphere weighs 500g,
what is the weight of each cube?

Cube = ________kg

/1

Answer these.

2. 2 x 7 = ______ **3.** 4 x 3 = ______ **4.** 6 x 6 = ______

5. 5 x 4 = ______ **6.** 9 x 3 = ______ **7.** 8 x 4 = ______

/6

Write in the missing numbers or words to complete each of these.

8. ______ → six hundred and five

9. 393 → ________________________________

10. ______ → nine hundred and thirty-seven

11. 412 → ________________________________

/4

Write each group of numbers in order starting with the smallest.

12. 743 778 760 704 ________________________________

13. 815 309 459 195 ________________________________

14. 236 655 530 632 ________________________________

15. 400 844 484 408 ________________________________

/4

Answer these.

16. 65 + 9 = ______________ 17. 28 + 7 = ______________

18. 57 + 6 = ______________ 19. 94 + 8= ______________

20. 32 + 9= ______________ 21. 73 + 8= ______________

/6

Complete the chart to show the numbers coming out of this subtraction machine.

		22.	23.	24	25.	26.
IN	65	91	42	77	59	83
OUT	35					

/5

Answer these.

27. How many sides does a hexagon have? ______________

28. How many sides does a pentagon have? ______________

29. Name two shapes with no straight sides. ______________

30. What is the name of shapes that have 3 straight sides? ______________

/4

31. What length is this line to the nearest half centimetre? Circle the correct answer.

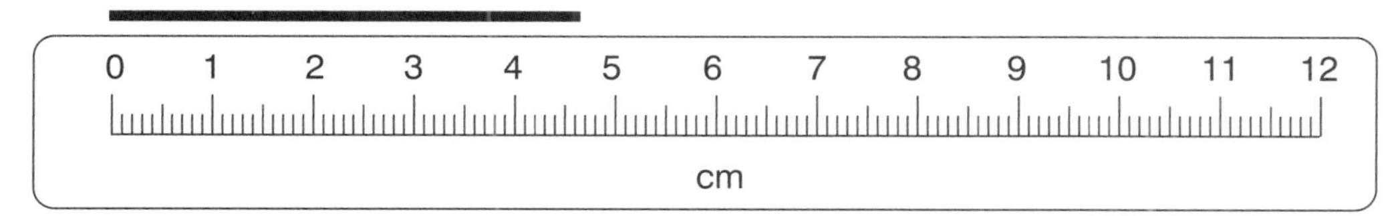

a) $4\frac{1}{2}$cm b) $5\frac{1}{2}$cm c) 5cm d) 4cm

/1

Answer these number problems.

32. I'm thinking of a number. If I add 8 to it the answer is 14. What is my number? ________

33. I'm thinking of a number. If I subtract 3 from it the answer is 9. What is my number? ________

34. I'm thinking of a number. If I add 60 to it the answer is 110. What is my number? ________

35. I'm thinking of a number. If I take away 40 from it the answer is 30.

What is my number? ____________

/4

36. There are 28 biscuits on a tray ready to be put in boxes. Each box holds 5 biscuits.

How many boxes are needed to hold all 28 biscuits? ____________

/1

How many minutes are there between these times?

37.  

____________ mins

38. 

10:15

____________ mins

/2

Complete these equivalent fraction chains.

39. $\frac{1}{2} \rightarrow \frac{\square}{4} \rightarrow \frac{\square}{6} \rightarrow \frac{\square}{8} \rightarrow \frac{\square}{10}$

40. $\frac{1}{3} \rightarrow \frac{2}{\square} \rightarrow \frac{3}{\square} \rightarrow \frac{4}{\square} \rightarrow \frac{5}{\square}$

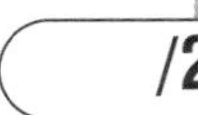

/40

PAPER 7

Write the next two numbers in each sequence.

1. 475	476	477	478	______	______
2. 364	363	362	361	______	______
3. 872	882	892	902	______	______
4. 519	509	499	489	______	______
5. 268	368	468	568	______	______
6. 931	831	731	631	______	______

/6

What times do these clocks show?

7.

______

8.

______

9.
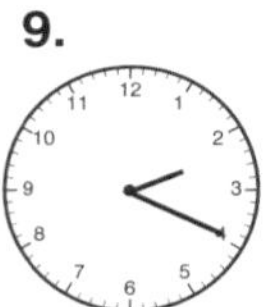
______

10.

______

11.
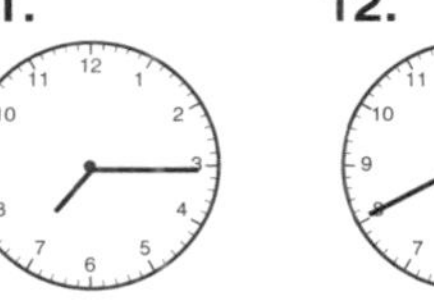
______

12.

______

/6

Answer these.

13. $\begin{array}{r} 43 \\ +\ 39 \\ \hline \end{array}$ ______

14. $\begin{array}{r} 65 \\ +\ 29 \\ \hline \end{array}$ ______

15. $\begin{array}{r} 37 \\ +\ 58 \\ \hline \end{array}$ ______

16. $\begin{array}{r} 29 \\ +\ 45 \\ \hline \end{array}$ ______

/4

17–19. Draw three different shapes on this grid, each with an area of exactly 12 squares, and label them A, B and C.

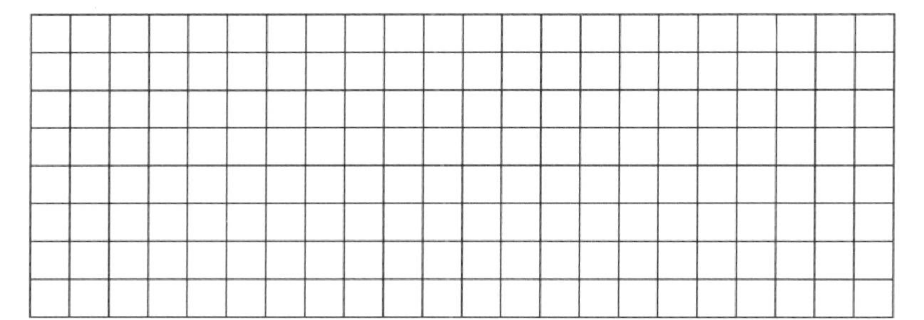

What is the perimeter of each shape?

20. A ______

21. B ______

22. C ______

/6

Use these numbers to answer the questions.

14 15 18 11 19

23. What is the largest <u>even</u> total made by adding two numbers? ____________

24. What is the smallest <u>odd</u> total made by adding two numbers? ____________

25. Which two numbers total 30? ____________

26. Which two numbers total 33? ____________

/4

Draw one line of symmetry on each shape.

27. **28.** **29.** **30.**

/4

Write the numbers shown on each abacus.

31. **32.** **33.** **34.**

/4

Write in the missing < or > signs for each pair of numbers.

35. 708 ☐ 807 **36.** 655 ☐ 635 **37.** 194 ☐ 941 **38.** 283 ☐ 322

/4

39. How much water is in this jug? Circle the correct answer.

5
0 litres

a) 5 litres

b) $2\frac{1}{2}$ litres

c) 3 litres

d) $3\frac{1}{2}$ litres

/1

40. Which is the smallest fraction? Circle the correct answer.

a) $\frac{1}{3}$ **b)** $\frac{1}{5}$ **c)** $\frac{1}{10}$ **d)** $\frac{1}{2}$

/1

/40

PAPER 8

1. What is the weight of this parcel? Circle the correct answer.

a) 2kg

b) 3kg

c) $2\frac{1}{4}$ kg

d) $2\frac{1}{2}$ kg

/1

All the digits 1 and 2 are missing. Complete these.

2.
```
   6 □
 − 3 7
 ─────
   □ 4
```

3.
```
   4 8
 − □ 6
 ─────
   3 □
```

4.
```
   6 □
 − 4 8
 ─────
   □ 4
```

/3

5. There are some chickens and 6 sheep in a field.
When all of the legs are counted, there are 34 legs.
How many chickens are there? ______________

/1

Underline the rectangle that shows an equivalent fraction to the fraction on the right. Then, write the equivalent fractions.

6. $\frac{\square}{\square} = \frac{1}{2}$

7. $\frac{\square}{\square} = \frac{1}{4}$

8. $\frac{\square}{\square} = \frac{1}{3}$

9. $\frac{\square}{\square} = \frac{1}{5}$

/4

These shapes are balanced.

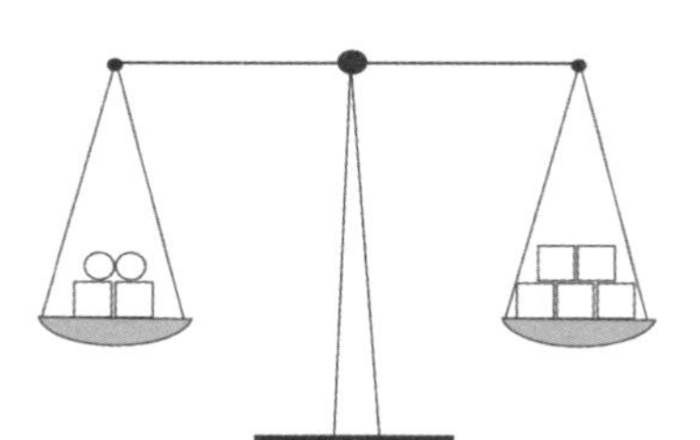

The total weight of 1 sphere and 1 cube is 5kg.
The sphere weighs 1kg more than the cube.

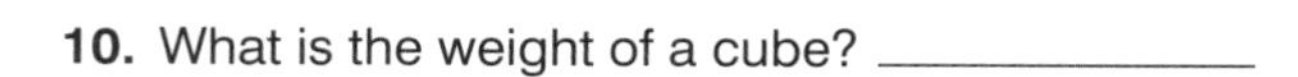

10. What is the weight of a cube? ______________

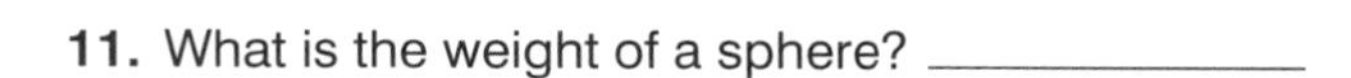

11. What is the weight of a sphere? ______________

12. What does each side of the balance weigh? ______________ /3

Answer these number problems.

13. I'm thinking of a number. If I add 3 to it the answer is 20. What is my number? ______

14. I'm thinking of a number. If I subtract 5 from it the answer is 10. What is my number? ______

15. I'm thinking of a number. If I add 40 to it the answer is 90. What is my number? ______

16. I'm thinking of a number. If I take away 70 from it the answer is 30.

What is my number? ______ /4

17. Circle the shape that has a line of symmetry.

a) **G** b) **J** c) **C** d) **F** /1

This graph shows the number of books that were read by some children.

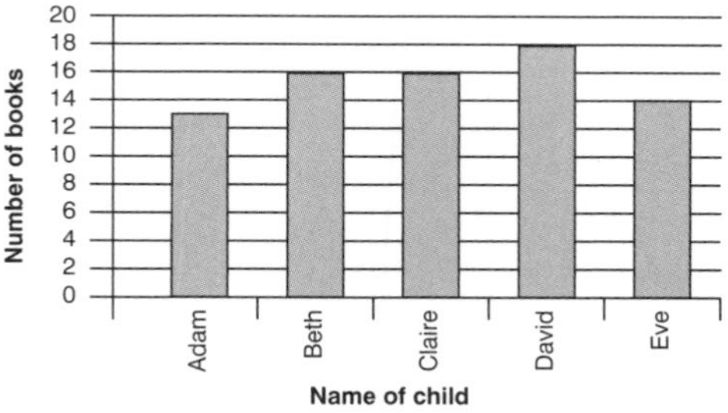

Number of books (0–20); Name of child: Adam, Beth, Claire, David, Eve

18. Who read 14 books? ______________

19. How many books did Beth read? ______________

20. How many more books did David read than Adam? ______________

21. Which two children read the same number of books? ______________

22. How many children read more than 15 books? ______________

23. How many books were read by this group altogether? ______________ /6

Write the numbers that went into this number machine.

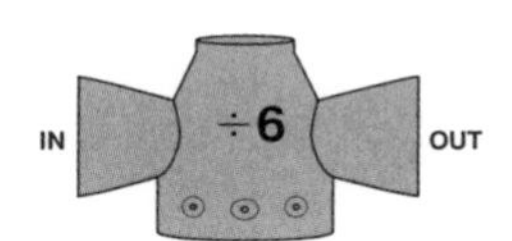

	24.	25.	26.	27.	28.
IN					
OUT	2	10	4	8	9

/5

29. Complete this multiplication grid.

X	7	5	8
10		50	
9			
3			

/1

30. Look at the fraction shaded for each circle. Write the fractions in order starting with the smallest.

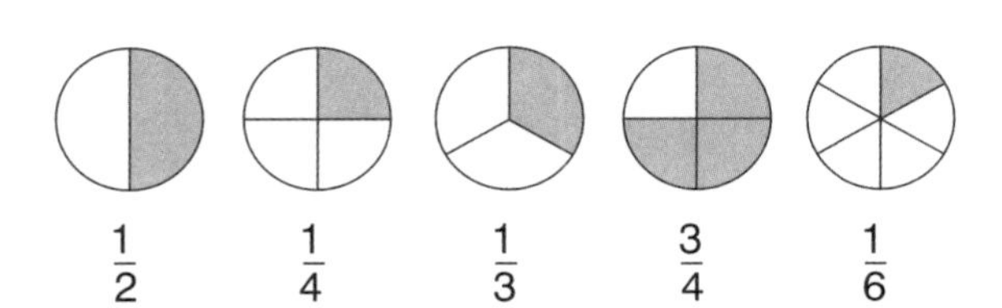

$\frac{1}{2}$ $\frac{1}{4}$ $\frac{1}{3}$ $\frac{3}{4}$ $\frac{1}{6}$

smallest ➔ _____ _____ _____ _____ _____ ➔ largest

/1

31. Becky filled a 17-litre tank with two different jugs. One jug held 3 litres and the other 4 litres. She used exactly 5 jugfuls to fill the tank. How many of each jug did she fill?

_____ 3 litre jugs _____ 4 litre jugs

/1

Answer these.

32. A lorry driver travels 53km in the morning and 37km in the afternoon.

How far does the lorry travel in total? __________

33. A postman has 109 letters and 16 parcels.

How many items altogether are there to deliver? __________

34. Jamal has read 90 pages of his reading book and there are 52 pages left.

How many pages in total are there in Jamal's reading book? __________

35. Julie is 136cm tall and her sister is 40cm taller than she is.

How tall is Julie's sister? ______________ /4

Choose from these shapes to answer the questions below.

prism cone cube cylinder sphere

36. Name 3 shapes with at least one curved face. ______________________

37. Name 2 shapes that have only flat faces. ______________________

38. Name a shape that has 6 identical square faces. ______________________

39. Name 2 shapes that have a least one flat circle face. ______________________

40. Name a shape with no flat faces. ______________________ /5

/40

PAPER 9

1. What fraction of the shape is shaded? Circle the correct answer.

a) $\frac{1}{3}$ b) $\frac{1}{5}$ c) $\frac{2}{3}$ d) $\frac{2}{5}$

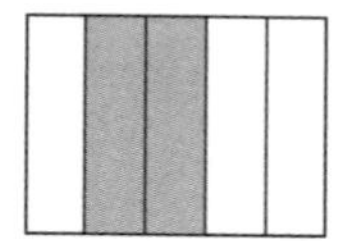

/1

The digits 1 to 8 are missing from these additions. Complete them with the digits in the correct place, using each digit once.

2.

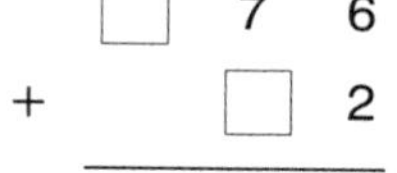

	□	7	6
+		□	2
	7	0	□

3.

		8	□
+		□	9
	1	3	1

4.

		9	□
+		□	4
	□	5	1

/3

Write the numbers shown on each abacus.

5. 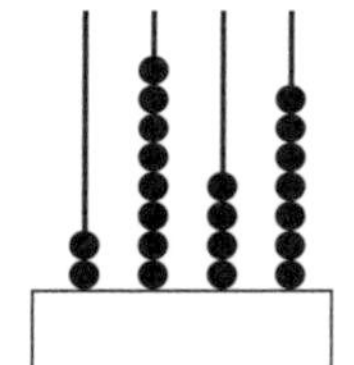

6. 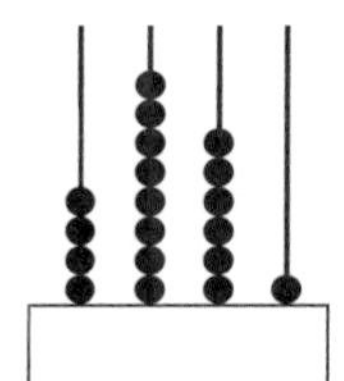

7. 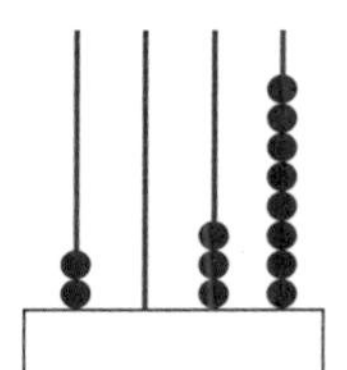

8. 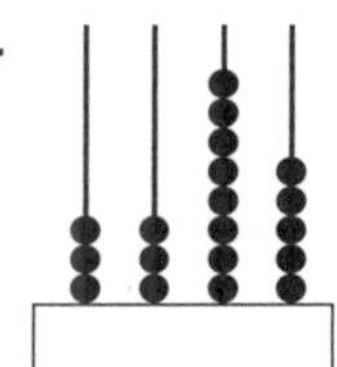

/4

Look at the number cards.

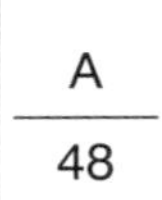

A	B	C	D	E
48	30	27	20	34

9. How much greater is A than B? ____________

10. What is the difference between C and E? ____________

11. Which number is 28 less than A? ____________

12. Which two numbers have a difference of 4? ____________

/4

13. What is the next number in this sequence? Fill in the correct answer.

427 437 447 457 ______

/1

14. A gardener is planning a path using 8 square tiles. Here are three designs using 8 squares. Draw 3 different path designs using 8 squares on the grid.

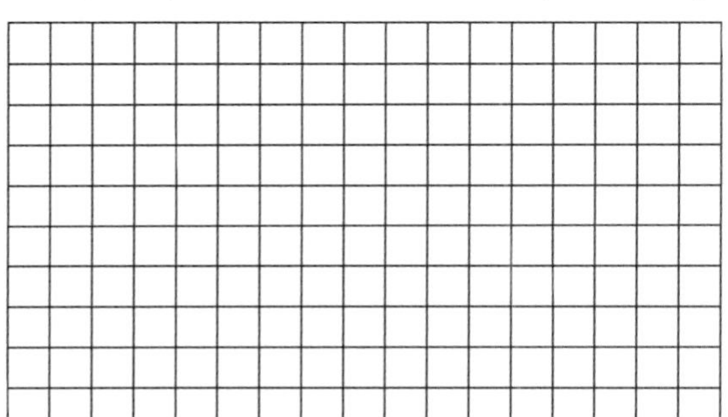

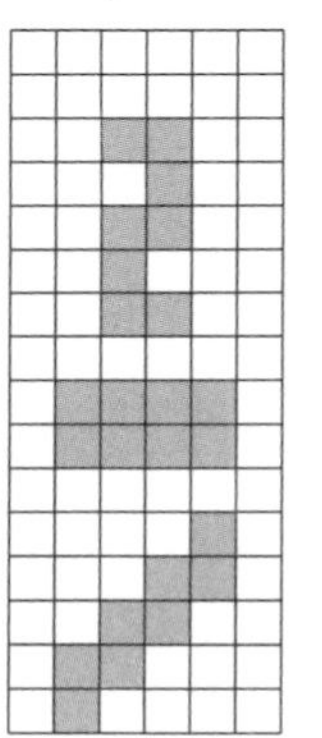

/1

15. What length is this line to the nearest $\frac{1}{2}$ centimetre? ☐ cm. /1

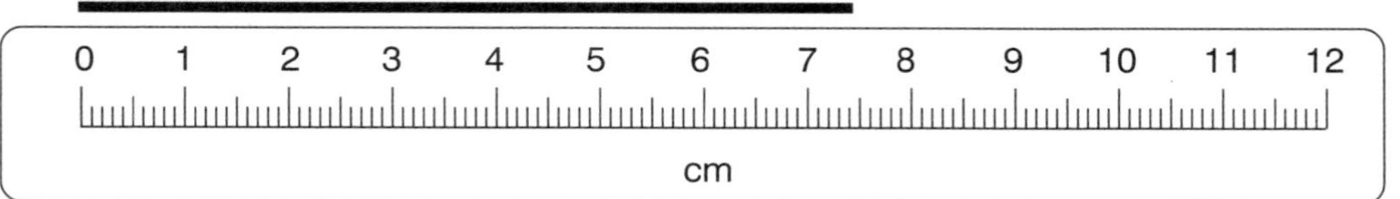

Read and answer these.

16. What is the difference between 28 and 48? ______

17. Subtract 16 from 43. ______

18. What number is 34 less than 52? ______

19. What is 80 take away 29? ______

20. How much greater is 91 than 76? ______ /5

How much water is there in each jug?

21.

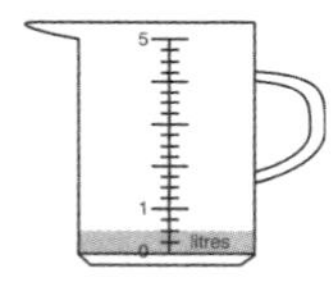

______

22.

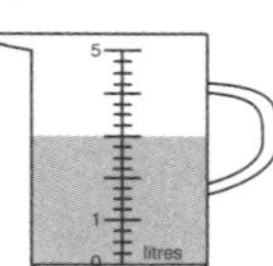

______

23.

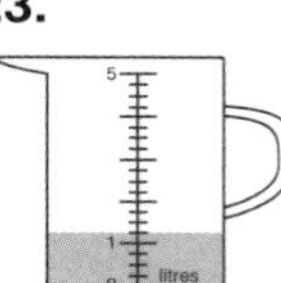

______

24.

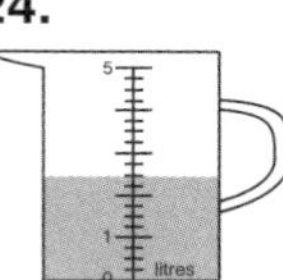

______

25.

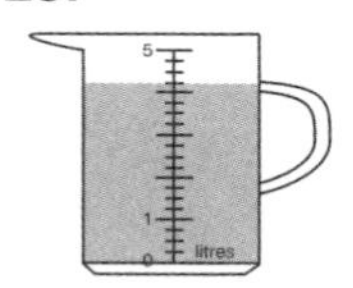

______

/5

Look at the shaded fraction of each shape. Write **less than** $\frac{1}{2}$ or **more than** $\frac{1}{2}$ for each part shaded.

26.

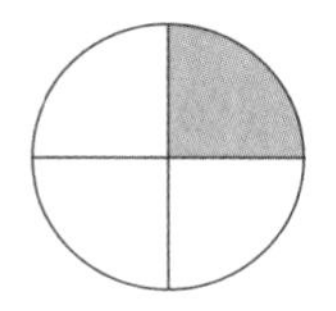

$\frac{1}{4}$ is ______ than $\frac{1}{2}$

27.

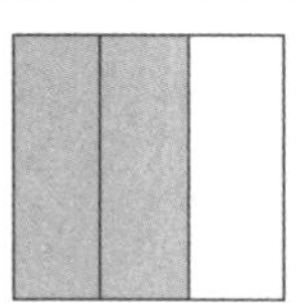

$\frac{2}{3}$ is ______ than $\frac{1}{2}$

28.

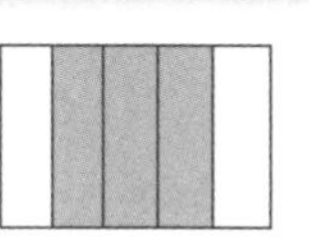

$\frac{3}{5}$ is ______ than $\frac{1}{2}$

29.

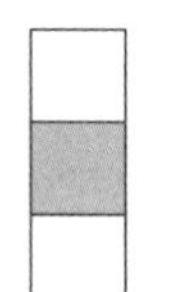

$\frac{1}{3}$ is ______ than $\frac{1}{2}$

30.

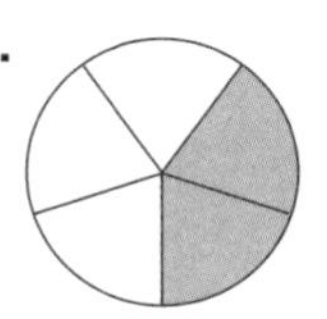

$\frac{2}{5}$ is ______ than $\frac{1}{2}$

/5

31. These shapes weigh 18kg altogether.
If each pyramid weighs 3kg, what is the weight of each cube?

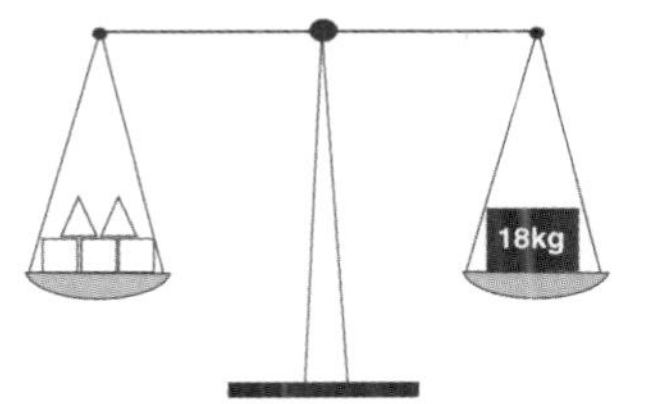

cube = ____________

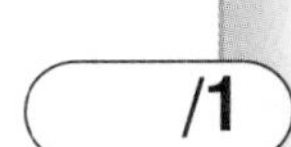

A group of children were asked about their favourite activities.

This graph shows the results.

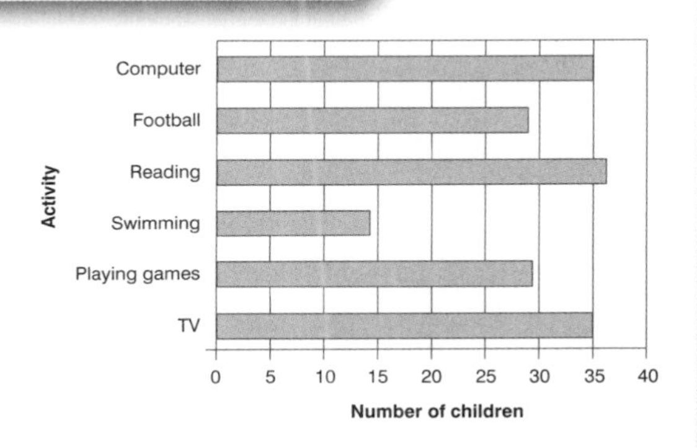

32. Which activity was chosen the most?

____

33. How many children chose swimming?

____

34. How many activities were chosen by more than 34 children? ____________

35. Which activity did 29 children choose? ____________

36. What was the total for using a computer and watching TV? ____________

/5

37. Complete this multiplication grid.

X	4	9	8
3		27	
6			
5			

/1

Write the name of these shapes.

38.

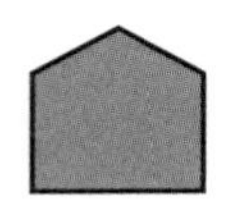

____

39.

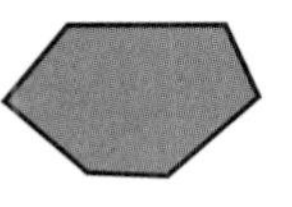

____

40.

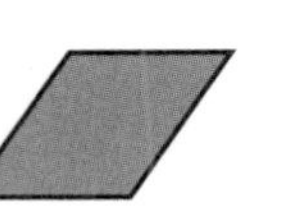

____

/40

PAPER 10

What is the next number in each of these sequences?

1. 13 17 21 25 ____________

2. 72 64 56 48 ____________

3. 34 45 56 67 ____________ /3

4. What is the difference between one thousand and nine hundred and ten? ______ /1

5. Circle three numbers that add together to make 150.

20 40 60 70 90 /1

Use either < or > to make these correct.

6. 23 + 6 ☐ 38 – 7 **7.** 3 x 8 ☐ 5 x 4 /2

This is part of a number line. Write in the missing numbers.

8–9.

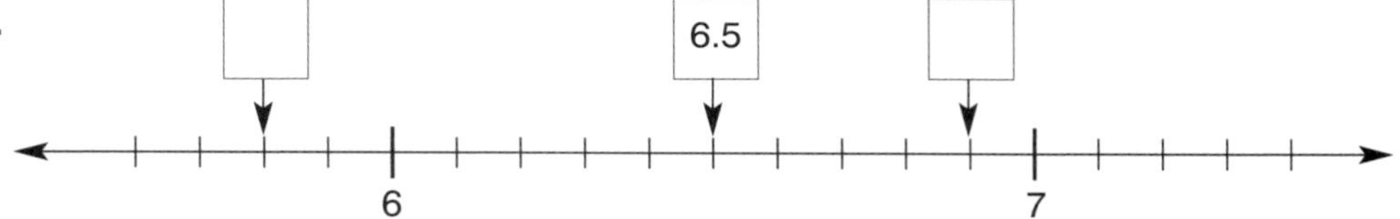

/2

Circle the two shapes that have two thirds shaded.

10–11.

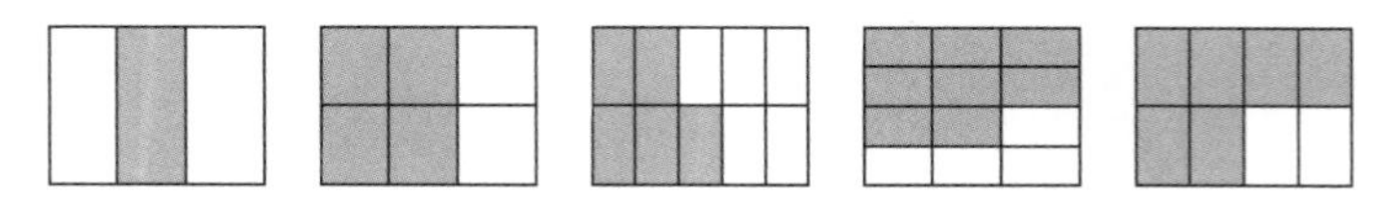

/2

Match each net to the name of a shape.

12. 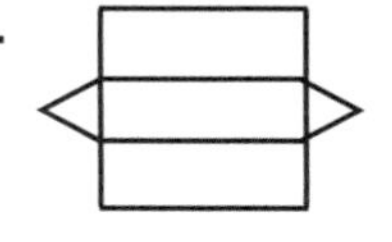

13. 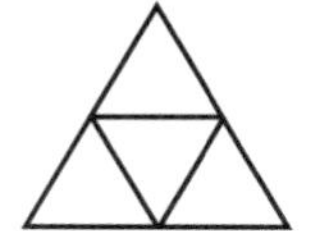

14. 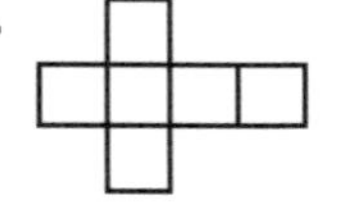

15. 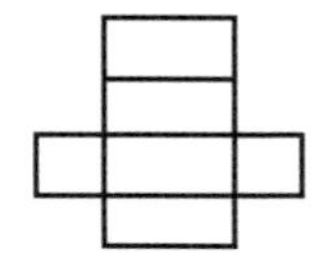

cuboid tetrahedron cube square based pyramid triangular prism /4

Look at these 5 angles.

16. Which is the largest angle? ________

17. Which is a right angle? ________

18. Which two angles are the same size? ________

19. Which of the angles is an obtuse angle? ________ /4

20. A square garden has a perimeter of 100 metres.
What is the length of one of its sides? ________ /1

21. What is double sixty-six? ________

22. What is half of 92? ________ /2

23. A film starts at 5.45pm and ends at 7.10pm.
For how many hours and minutes does the film last for? ________ /1

Measure the length of each line.

24. ______ cm

25. ______ cm

26. ______ cm

27. ______ cm

28. What is the total length of the four lines? ______ cm /5

29. A box of 4 light-bulbs costs £3.56. What is the cost of each bulb? ____________ /1

What is the missing number for each of these?

30. 358 – ________ = 180

31. 72 ÷ ________ = 8

32. 40 + 95 + ________ = 230

33. 6 x ________ = 108 /4

34. Draw a regular hexagon on this circle.

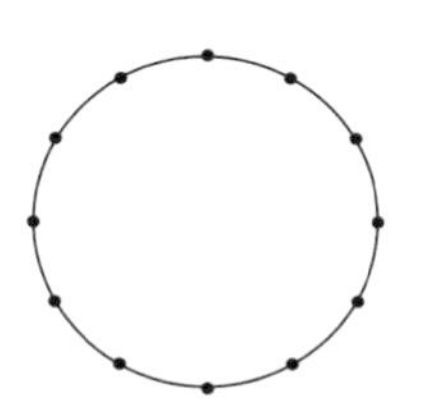

/1

What is the weight of the fruit on these scales?

35.

____

36.

____

/2

This bar chart shows the number of stickers collected by some children.

37. Who has collected 38 stickers?

____

38. How many more stickers has David collected than Nick?

____

Child's name: Amy, David, Sam, Nick, Megan

0 5 10 15 20 25 30 35 40 45 50

Number of stickers

/2

This grid has a shaded shape drawn on it.

39. What is the area shaded on this grid? ________ squares

40. Draw a shape on the grid with an area of half the size of the shaded shape.

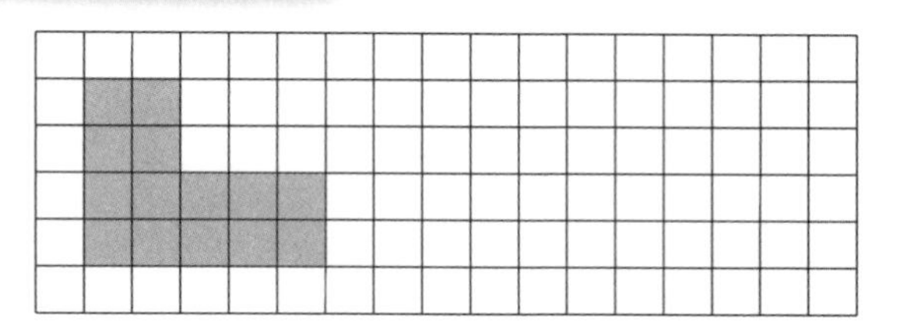

/2

/40

PAPER 11

1. Circle the number which is seven thousand and fourteen.

a) 7140 **b)** 7014 **c)** 70014 **d)** 700014

/1

Write the number shown on each abacus.

2.

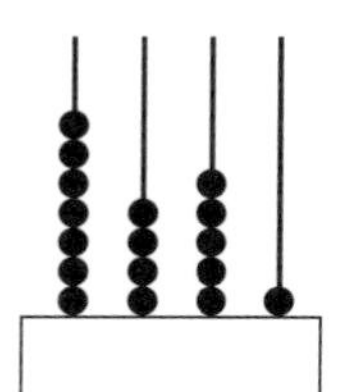

3.

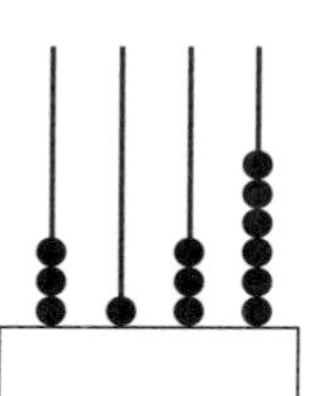

4.

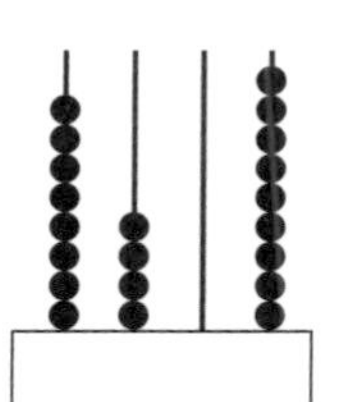

5.

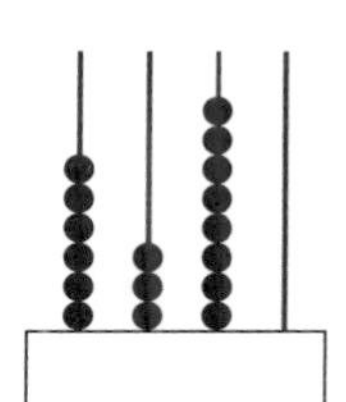

/4

6. Which shape is symmetrical? Circle the correct answer.

a)

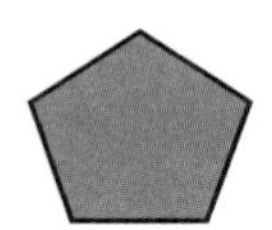

b)

c)

d)

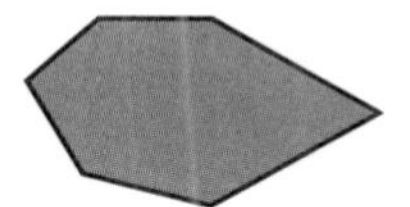

/1

Write in the next two numbers.

7. 450 500 550 600 650 ___ ___

8. 720 710 700 690 680 ___ ___

9. 350 325 300 275 250 ___ ___

10. 159 162 165 168 171 ___ ___

/4

11. What number is the arrow pointing to? Circle the correct answer.

a) 15.2 **b)** 16.4 **c)** 15.4 **d)** 15.6

/1

Draw two rectangles with the same perimeter as this square.

12–13.

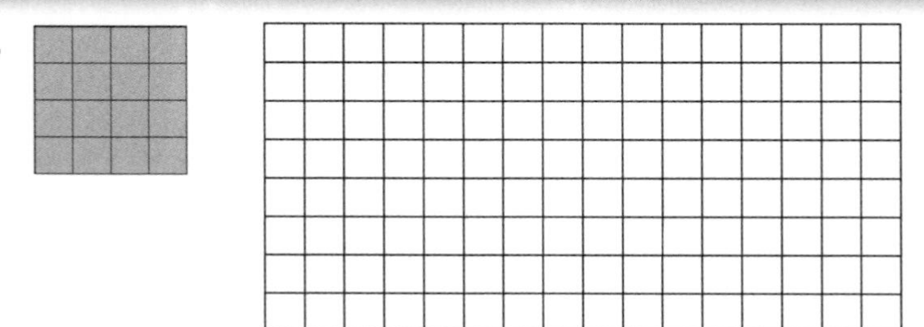

/2

Draw two different shapes with the same perimeter as the square. They do not need to be rectangles.

14–15.

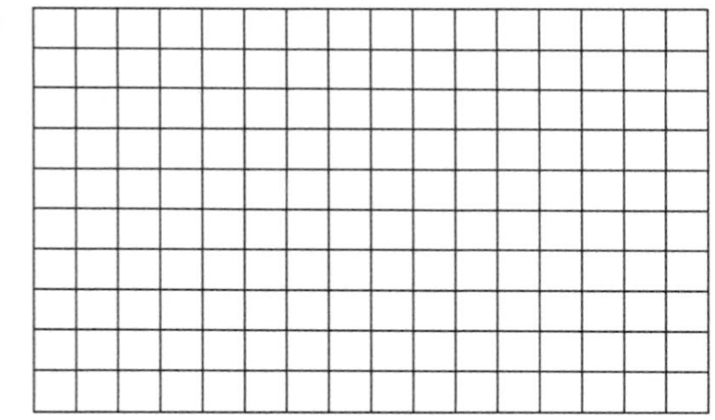

/2

Write these numbers in the correct places to make each sentence true.

16. 5650 8650 ________ is less than ________.

17. 4139 4317 ________ is less than ________.

18. 5012 5021 ________ is less than ________.

19. 3806 8312 ________ is less than ________.

/4

Round these to the nearest 100 and write in the answers.

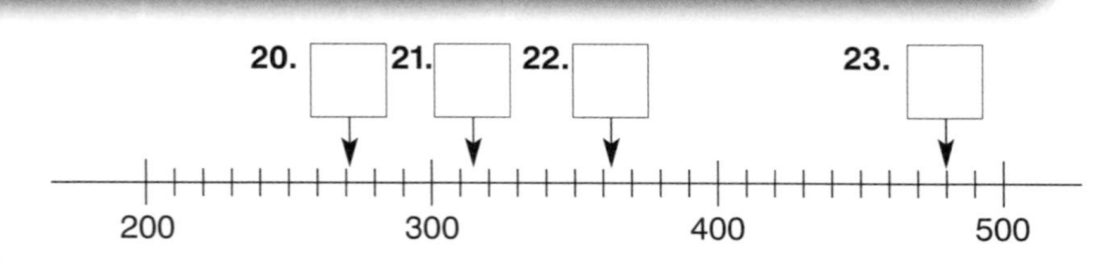

/4

Write these fractions as decimals.

24. $5\frac{3}{10}$ ____________ **25.** $\frac{7}{10}$ ____________ **26.** $8\frac{4}{10}$ ____________

27. $3\frac{5}{10}$ ____________ **28.** $9\frac{1}{10}$ ____________

/5

29. Which of these has 6 faces? Circle the correct answer.

a) 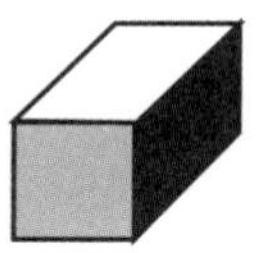
b) 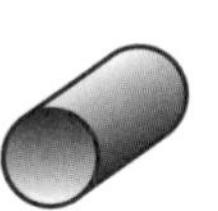
c) 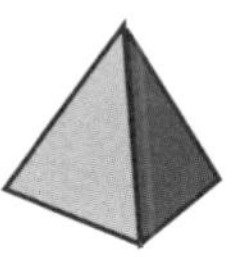
d) 

/1

Complete the table.

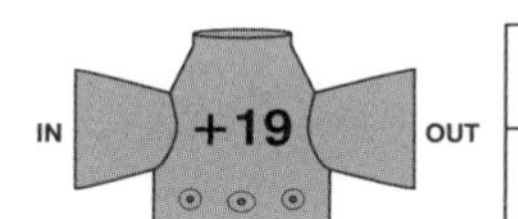

	30.	31.	32.	33.	34.	35.
IN	6		17		18	
OUT		22		35		47

/6

Write these times.

36. 
37. 
38. 
39. 

____________ ____________ ____________ ____________

/4

40. What is the missing number? 35 ÷ ☐ = 7

/1

/40

PAPER 12

1. Write the next number in this sequence. 34 42 50 58 ___ /1

2. What length is 340cm in metres and centimetres? Circle the correct answer.

   a) 34m 10cm **b)** 3m 40cm **c)** 3m 4cm **d)** 34m 100cm /1

3. Use a ruler to join dots to make a triangle with no right angles.

   • • •

   • • •

   • • • /1

Write in the missing numbers.

4. 5931 = 5000 + ______ + 30 + ______

5. 2379 = ______ + 300 + ______ + 9

6. 6462 = 6000 + ______ + 60 + ______

7. 6723 = ______ + 700 + 20 + ______

8. 4814 = 4000 + ______ + 10 + ______

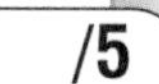

/5

9. The digits 3, 4, 5 and 6 can be arranged to make the number 4563. Rearrange these four digits to make six different numbers. Write the numbers in order, starting with the smallest.

______ ______ ______ ______ ______ ______

/1

Complete this chart.

Shape	Name of shape	Number of faces	Number of corners	Number of edges
10.	Cube			
11.	Cuboid			
12.	Triangular prism			

/3

Answer booklet Maths 8–9

PAPER 1

1. c) 16
2. 115
3. seventy–one
4. 426
5. five hundred and twenty–six
6. 219
7. 47, 52
8. 95, 97
9. 76, 79
10. 64, 68
11. 9
12. 8
13. 18
14. 4
15. a) 6 squares
16. cylinders, cone
17. cubes, sphere
18. spheres, cylinder
19. cuboids, prism
20. 2
21. 5
22. 10
23. 20
24. $\frac{1}{4}$
25. $\frac{1}{3}$
26. $\frac{1}{6}$
27. $\frac{1}{8}$
28. $\frac{1}{5}$
29. $\frac{1}{9}$
30. 6cm
31. 8cm
32. 5cm
33. 28
34. 16
35. 10
36. 16
37. 30
38. 6.15
39. 3.45
40. 5.30

PAPER 2

1. b) 400
2. 921
3. 408
4. 715
5. 647
6. 7. 8.

9. 500ml
10. 4
11. 6
12. 6
13. 7
14. clock c)
15. 2kg
16. 5000g
17. 4 litres
18. 6000ml
19. c) 6 squares
20. 80, 76
21. 13, 8
22. 63, 61
23. 40, 37

Name of shape	Total number of faces	Number of square faces	Number of rectangle faces	Number of triangular faces
24. Cube	6	6	0	0
25. Cubiod	6	2	4	0
26. Triangular prism	5	0	3	2

27. 60
28. 900
29. 50
30. 200
31. 39
32. 66
33. 44
34. 48
35. 56
36. 86
37. c) $\frac{1}{6}$
38. 45
39. 6
40. 50

PAPER 3

1. 90, 8
2. 200, 10, 7
3. 400, 50, 2
4. 600, 80, 3
5. 100, 60, 5
6. 700, 0, 9
7. >
8. <
9. >
10. >
11. triangle b)
12. 13kg
13. 8
14. 2 litres
15. $1\frac{1}{2}$ litres
16. $\frac{1}{2}$ litre
17. 13
18. 3.45
19. 12.15
20. 5.00
21. $1\frac{1}{2}$ hours
22. 12, 25, 59, 91
23. 73, 78, 83, 87
24. 22, 39, 45, 68
25. 10, 16, 60, 61

26–28. There are many possible combinations:
7+8, 9+10, 6+5 or
6+9, 10+8, 5+7 or
10+5, 9+8, 6+7

29. 68
30. 7
31. 46
32. 42
33. 24
34. 41
35. 56
36. 38
37. 68
38. 52
39. c) is a sphere
40. c) 9 cm

PAPER 4

1. 60, 8
2. 500, 9
3. 800, 50
4. 600, 20, 5
5. <
6. >
7. =
8. <
9. <
10. =
11. c) 25 squares
12. 2kg
13. clock a)

14. 3x4=12, 2x5=10, 5x8=40
15. 507
16. 364
17. 258
18. 683
19. 37, 57
20. 23, 35
21. 51, 56
22. 98, 78
23. 94, 88
24. 26, 41
25. circle
26. triangle
27. pentagon
28. oval
29. hexagon
30. $\frac{1}{4}$
31. $\frac{1}{2}$
32. $\frac{1}{6}$
33. $\frac{1}{3}$
34. $\frac{1}{5}$
35. b) 6
36. 7
37.

x	7	3	9
5	35	15	45
4	28	12	36

38. 4
39. 5
40. 9

PAPER 5

1. 10
2. 9
3. 5
4. 2
5. 4
6. 7kg
7. 8000ml
8. 3m
9. 6km
10. c) 301
11. 5
12. 1kg 250g
13. 255
14. 560
15. 461
16. 90
17. 24
18. 7
19. 600
20. 700
21. hexagons, rectangle
22. triangles, semi–circle
23. quadrilaterals, pentagon
24. ovals, circle
25. 2cm
26. 8cm
27. 5cm
28. 3
29. 8
30. 8
31. 60
32. 7
33. 12
34. Thursday
35. Saturday
36. April
37. $5cm^2$
38. $8cm^2$
39. $11cm^2$
40. b) cylinder

PAPER 6

1. 2kg
2. 14
3. 12
4. 36
5. 20
6. 27
7. 32
8. 605
9. three hundred and ninety–three
10. 937
11. four hundred and twelve
12. 704, 743, 760, 778
13. 195, 309, 459, 815
14. 236, 530, 632, 655
15. 400, 408, 484, 844
16. 74
17. 35
18. 63
19. 102
20. 41
21. 81
22–26. 61,12, 47, 29, 53
27. 6
28. 5
29. oval and circle
30. triangles
31. 4.5cm
32. 6
33. 12
34. 50
35. 70
36. 6
37. 30
38. 15
39. $\frac{1}{2} \rightarrow \frac{2}{4} \rightarrow \frac{3}{6} \rightarrow \frac{4}{8} \rightarrow \frac{5}{10}$
40. $\frac{1}{3} \rightarrow \frac{2}{6} \rightarrow \frac{3}{9} \rightarrow \frac{4}{12} \rightarrow \frac{5}{15}$

PAPER 7

1. 479, 480
2. 360, 359
3. 912, 922
4. 479, 469
5. 668, 768
6. 531, 431
7. 4.10
8. 10.35
9. 2.20
10. 6.55
11. 7.15
12. 1.40
13. 82
14. 94
15. 95
16. 74
17–22. Check drawings and answers.
23. 34
24. 25
25. 11, 19
26. 15, 18 or 14, 19
27. **28.**
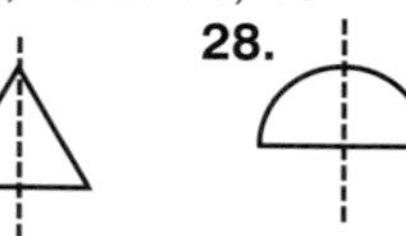
29.

30.
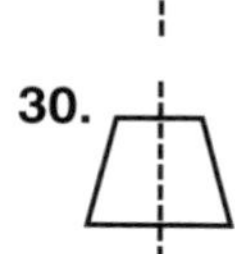
31. 247
32. 983
33. 208
34. 675
35. $<$
36. $>$
37. $<$
38. $<$
39. d) $3\frac{1}{2}$ litres
40. $\frac{1}{10}$

PAPER 8

1. c) $2\frac{1}{2}$ kg
2. 61–37=24
3. 48–16=32
4. 62–48=14
5. 5
6. $\frac{2}{4}$
7. $\frac{2}{8}$
8. $\frac{3}{9}$
9. $\frac{2}{10}$
10. 2kg
11. 3kg
12. 10kg
13. 17
14. 15
15. 50
16. 100
17. shape c)
18. Eve
19. 16
20. 5
21. Beth and Claire
22. 3
23. 77
24. 12
25. 60
26. 24
27. 48
28. 54
29.

x	7	5	8
10	70	50	80
9	63	45	72
3	21	15	24

30. $\frac{1}{6}$, $\frac{1}{4}$, $\frac{1}{3}$, $\frac{1}{2}$, $\frac{3}{4}$
31. 3 3 litre jugs and 2 4 litre jugs
32. 90km
33. 125
34. 142
35. 176cm
36. cylinder, sphere, cone
37. cube, cuboid
38. cube
39. cone, cylinder
40. sphere

PAPER 9

1. d) $\frac{2}{5}$
2. 676 + 32= 708
3. 82+49 = 131
4. 97+54 = 151
5. 2847
6. 4861
7. 2038
8. 3385
9. 18
10. 7
11. 20
12. 30 and 34
13. 467
14. Check all shapes have 8 squares.
15. $7\frac{1}{2}$ cm
16. 20
17. 27
18. 18
19. 51
20. 15
21. $\frac{1}{2}$ litre or 500ml
22. 3 litres
23. $1\frac{1}{4}$ litres
24. $2\frac{1}{2}$ litres
25. $4\frac{1}{4}$ litres
26. less than $\frac{1}{2}$
27. more than $\frac{1}{2}$
28. more than $\frac{1}{2}$
29. less than $\frac{1}{2}$
30. less than $\frac{1}{2}$
31. 4 kg
32. reading
33. 14
34. 3
35. playing games
36. 70
37.

x	4	9	8
3	12	27	24
6	24	54	48
5	20	45	40

38. pentagon
39. hexagon
40. parallelogram

PAPER 10

1. 29
2. 40
3. 78
4. 90
5. 20, 40, 90
6. <
7. >
8. 5.8
9. 6.9
10. –11.
11. 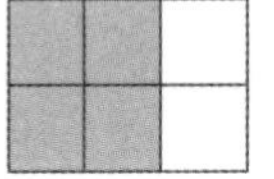 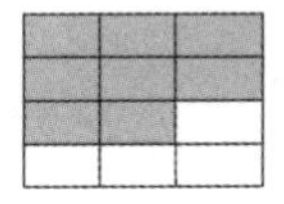
12. triangular prism
13. tetrahedron
14. cube
15. cuboid
16. D
17. C
18. B and E
19. D
20. 25m
21. 132
22. 46
23. 1 hour 25 minutes
24. 8cm
25. 3cm
26. 9cm
27. 7cm
28. 27cm
29. 89p
30. 178
31. 9
32. 95
33. 18
34. Check every other dot has been joined to make a regular hexagon. 
35. 480g (Accept answer between 470g and 490g.)
36. 2kg 800g or 2.8kg
37. Sam
38. 15
39. 14
40. Check the shape covers 7 squares.

PAPER 11

1. b) 7014
2. 7451
3. 3136
4. 8409
5. 6380
6. shape a)
7. 700, 750
8. 670, 660
9. 225, 200
10. 174. 177
11. c) 15.4

12–15. Check each shape has a perimeter of 16 squares.
16. 5650 is less than 8650
17. 4139 is less than 4317
18. 5012 is less than 5021
19. 3086 is less than 8312
20. 300
21. 300
22. 400
23. 500
24. 5.3
25. 0.7
26. 8.4
27. 3.5
28. 9.1
29. shape a)
30. 25
31. 3
32. 36
33. 16
34. 37
35. 28
36. 2.15
37. 7.40
38. 4.20
39. 10.55
40. 5

PAPER 12

1. 66
2. b) 3m 40cm
3. Check the triangle has no right angles.
4. 900, 1
5. 2000, 70
6. 400, 2
7. 6000, 3
8. 800, 4
9. There are many possible solutions. Check all numbers use the digits 3,4,5 and 6 and are listed in size order. EG 3456, 3465, 3546, 3564, 5364, 5634

10–12.

Shape	Name of shape	Number of faces	Number of corners	Number of edges
10.	Cube	6	8	12
11.	Cuboid	6	8	12
12.	Triangular prism	5	6	9

13. 18
14. 36
15. 42
16. 30
17. 24
18. 48
19. 54
20. 850
21. 420
22. 5050
23. 4680
24. 1475
25. symmetrical
26. symmetrical
27. not symmetrical
28. symmetrical
29. symmetrical
30. not symmetrical
33. 152
32. 144
33. 145
34. 292
35. Length = 3cm, width = 2cm, Perimeter = 10cm
36. Length = 4cm, width = 3cm, Perimeter = 14cm
37. Length = 4cm, width = 2cm, Perimeter = 12cm
38. Length = 3cm, width = 5cm, Perimeter = 16cm
39. 494
40. 915ml

PAPER 13

1. 21
2. 12
3. 4
4. 6
5. 8
6. 4
7. c) 3604
8. b) –25
9. $20\frac{6}{10}$ or $20\frac{3}{5}$
10. $4\frac{9}{10}$
11. $\frac{8}{10}$ or $\frac{4}{5}$
12. $7\frac{2}{10}$ or $7\frac{1}{5}$
13. $16\frac{5}{10}$ or $16\frac{1}{2}$
14. 100kg
15. 3 litres
16. 3 litres
17. 150
18. 160
19. 180
20. 190
21. 46
22. 18
23. 55
24. 23
25. 43
26. 32
27. 2.35
28. 7.40
29. 4.10
30. 10.15
31. 1.55
32. 7.25
33. 2
34. 10
35. 4
36. 20
37. 4
38. 5
39. 34m
40. 24m

PAPER 14

1.

2	×	9	→	18
×		×		
6	×	5	→	30
↓		↓		
12		45		

2. 5
3. 312
4. 313
5. 436
6. 362
7. 176
8. 366
9. 1
10. 2
11. 1
12. 1
13. a) 800
14. 289 +614 = 903
15. 602 + 349 = 951
16. 284+ 467=751
17. 3451
18. 3116
19. 4406
20. b)9cm
21. d) 5cm
22. 6039, 4039
23. 620, 640
24. 185, 245

25. 1500, 1450
26. 1993, 1793
27. 230
28. 380
29. 320
30. 230
31. 40
32. 70
33. 310
34. B
35. 6kg
36. $3\frac{1}{2}$kg
37. $5\frac{1}{2}$kg
38. $8\frac{1}{2}$kg
39. A
40. B

PAPER 15

1. a) 12.7
2. 5000, 80
3. 900, 40
4. 8000, 200
5. 1597, 1637
6. 4702, 5002
7. 3113, 3003
8. 5145, 5195
9. 1060, 1030
10. d) 36 square centimetres
11. 8
12. 172+658 = 830
13. 10.25
14. 10.50
15. 11.10
16. 11.25
17. 11.35
18. 12.00
19. <
20. <
21. >
22. >
23. >
24. >
25. 262
26. 235
27. 424
28. 469
29. 459
30. 278
31. c) 490
32. elephant
33. blue whale
34. rabbit
35. 25 years
36. cat
37. 35 years
38. dolphin
39. 30m
40. 38m

PAPER 16

1. 9m 22cm
2. 150cm
3. 2m 80cm
4. 325cm
5. 7m 5cm
6. 609cm
7. 7.50pm
8. 8.25am
9. 5.30pm
10. 40 minutes
11. c) prism
12. 450ml
13. 3054
14. 6739
15. 5508
16. 4290
17. 953 and 957
18. 975 and 995
19. 1220 and 820
20. >
21. <
22. <
23. >
24. >
25. >
26. True
27. False
28. True
29. False
30. True
31. 56
32. 8
33. 4
34. 12
35. 7
36. 9
37. 6
38. 6
39. 67
40. 42p, £1.05, 35p

Paper 17

1. 61
2. 184
3. 74
4. 158
5.

3	×	7	→	21
×		×		
9	×	5	→	45
↓		↓		
27		35		

6. 6kg
7. 2.40
8. 7.25
9. 11.50
10. 8.45
11. 1610
12. 1740
13. 1780
14. 1840
15. 15
16. 31
17. 26
18. 27
19. 37
20. 42
21. 7052, 7162, 7692, 7962
22. 5200, 5800, 6100, 6900
23. 9371, 9407, 9417, 9470
24. 8408, 8804, 8840, 8880
25. b) 3
26. 948
27. 896
28. 452
29. 801
30. 371
31. 493
32. 119
33. 277
34. 224
35. 130
36. 288
37. 180
38. 144 hours
39. d) –3°
40.

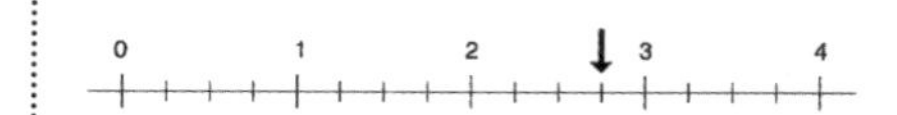

PAPER 18

1. 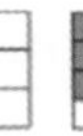 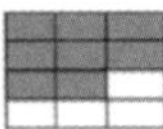
2. 85, 30, 55
3. 9034, 9014
4. 1588, 1590
5. 3206, 2206
6. 6505, 6500
7. 2391, 3928, 5076, 8431
8. 4032, 5993, 9042, 9053
9. 3506, 4021, 5070, 5072
10. 3189, 8931, 9138, 9813
11. a) quadrilateral
12. 16cm
13. Adam
14. Sam
15. 9
16. Joanne
17. Hannah
18. 372
19. 385
20. 393
21. 408
22. 417
23. 12
24. 112
25. 129
26. 108
27. 161
28. B
29. B
30. D
31. A
32. C
33. 36 centimetres
34. 77 square centimetres
35. 42 centimetres
36. 108 square centimetres
37. Family ticket £70
38. 1 adult and 3 child tickets £64
39. 2 adult and 1 child ticket £68
40. c) 12

PAPER 19

1. 790
2. 1980
3. 620
4. 3475
5. 2050
6. 1080
7. 2.17 (accept 2.16)
8. 7.48
9. 10.51
10. 3.26
11. b) 7.3
12. £560
13. £360
14. £84
15. =
16. <
17. <
18. >
19. 600ml
20. 250ml
21. 450ml
22. 850ml
23. 9 squares
24. 12 squares
25. 14 squares
26. 11 squares
27. 260
28. 260
29. 280
30. 290
31. 8700m
32. 6135m
33. 4km 650m
34. 10 008m
35. 4050m
36. 9km 45m
37. 4
38. 2
39. 2
40. 3

PAPER 20

1. 8305
2. 8311
3. 8325
4. 8336
5. 21
6. 2
7. 240
8. 10
9. 60
10. 10
11.

x	7	3	8
9	63	27	72
4	28	12	32
5	35	15	40

12. 4 drinks and 5 cakes
13. 2 acute, 1 obtuse, 0 right angles
14. 1 acute, 1 obtuse, 2 right angles
15. 3 acute, 0 obtuse, 0 right angles
16. 2 acute, 2 obtuse, 0 right angles

17–20.

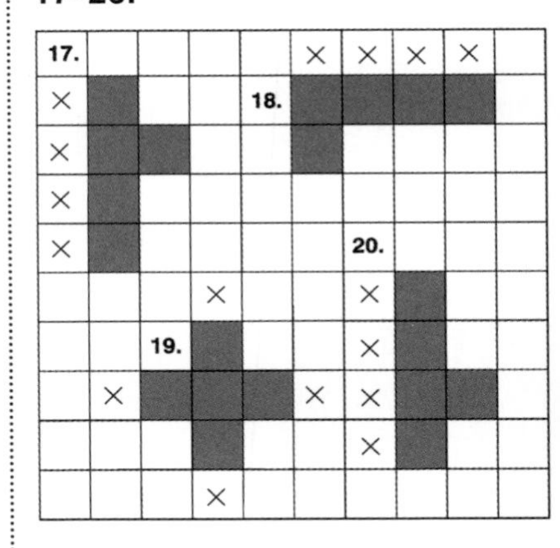

21. 31
22. 26
23. 39
24. 50
25. 34
26. 42
27. 9
28. 11
29. 2 8 + 1 4 = 4 2
30. 2 7 + 1 6 = 4 3
31. 5 x 9 = 4 5
32. 8 x 3 = 2 4
33. 7 0 – 2 5 = 4 5
34. 8 6 – 5 4 = 3 2
35. A and C
36. D
37. B and D
38. A and B
39. 14cm
40. 16cm

PAPER 21

1. 72 or 78
2. shape c)
3. 4
4. 11
5. 7
6. 8
7. 36

8. 3
9. A
10. B
11. 7kg
12. 6.12
13. 8.34
14. 11.52
15. 1.08
16. 1600
17. 1800
18. 1800
19. 1900
20. a) 9445
21. 42, 27, 45
22. $\frac{3}{4}$
23.

Angle	23.	24.	25.	26.	27.	28.
Acute	✓			✓		
Obtuse		✓				✓
Right-angled			✓		✓	

29. 54
30. 144
31. 200
32. 230
33. 13
34. 16
35. 15
36. 23
37. Check area is 14 squares (2x7 rectangle).
38. 18
39. Check area is 18 squares (2x9 or 3x6 rectangle).
40. 22 (2x9 rectangle) or 18 (3x6 rectangle).

PAPER 22

1. $\frac{9}{24}$
2. $\frac{4}{18}$
3. $\frac{6}{16}$
4. 2200
5. 2200
6. 4650
7. 4700
8. 6330
9. 6300
10. 5620
11. 5600
12. c) 8080m
13. 201
14. 301
15. 2004
16. 2351
17. 3013
18. c) 7
19. 1501
20. 1181
21. 1474
22. 1540
23. £7.20
24. cuboid
25. cube
26. square based pyramid
27. tetrahedron

	Symmetrical	Not symmetrical
Some right angles	28.	29.
No right angles	30.	31.

32. (802) 810 811 809
33. 756 765 (755) 766
34. 490 488 486 (480)
35. 24cm²
36. 22cm
37. 28cm²
38. 22cm
39. 45cm²
40. 28cm

PAPER 23

1. 31
2. 173
3. 508
4. 277
5. 237
6. 32
7. 19
8. 28
9. 21
10. 26
11. 2.5cm
12. 7cm
13. 12
14. 8
15. 10
16. 6
17. 170, 185, 215
18. 206, 200, 198
19. 330, 335, 340
20. 230, 260, 350
21. c) 3
22. £56
23. 123
24. 137
25. 84
26. 157
27. b) 8
28. Check scale shows 650g.
29. 894 – 352 = 542
30. 849 –326 = 523
31. 583 – 431 = 152
32. isosceles triangles
33. right–angled triangles
34. equilateral triangles
35. 40
36. Thursday
37. 15
38. 65
39. 1010
40. 1110

PAPER 24

1. 27
2. 28
3. 25
4. 48
5. 6
6. west
7. north
8. south
9. south
10. c) $8\frac{2}{5}$
11. 3700, 3750
12. 6470, 6460
13. 1925, 1900
14. 1174, 1177
15. >
16. <
17. <
18. <
19. 278
20. 393
21. 218
22. 625
23. 2500ml or 2.5 Litres
24. 1250ml or 1.25ml
25. 3250ml or 3.25 litres

26. 4750ml or 4.75 litres
27. 4703
28. 3805
29. 5466
30. 9.27
31. 2.53
32. 12.20
33. 8.06
34. b) 1466
35. 2 square faces, 4 rectangle faces
36. 2 circle faces, 1 curved face
37. 1 square face, 4 triangle faces
38. a) 5
39. 15
40. 22

Complete the results table of the numbers coming out of this function machine.

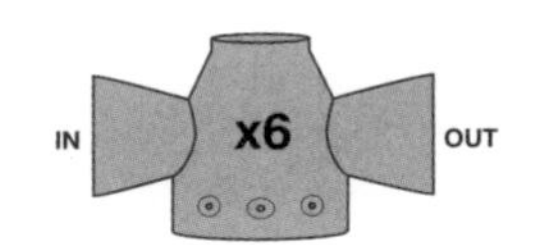

	13.	14.	15.	16.	17.	18.	19.
IN	3	6	7	5	4	8	9
OUT							

/7

Write the halfway numbers for each of these number lines.

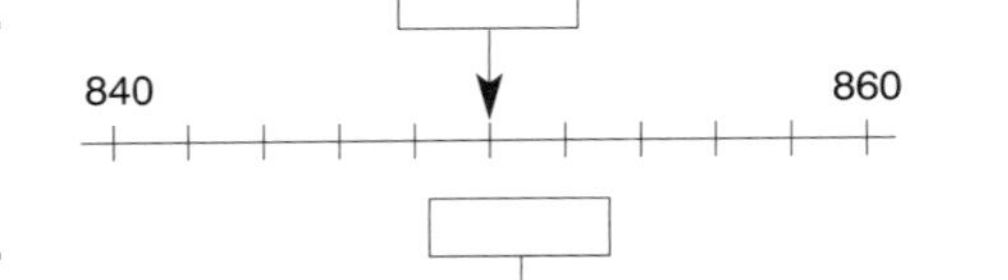

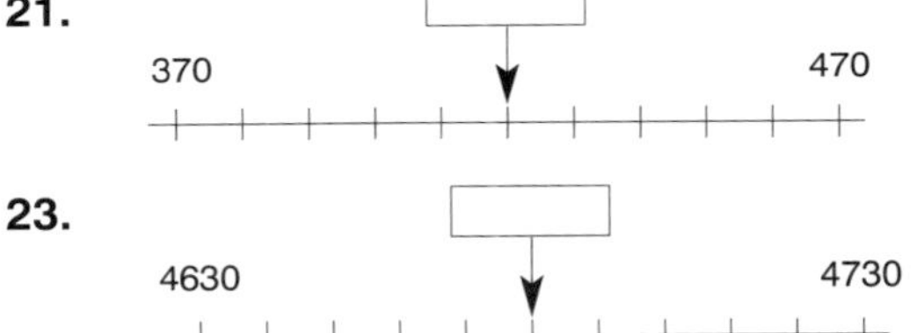

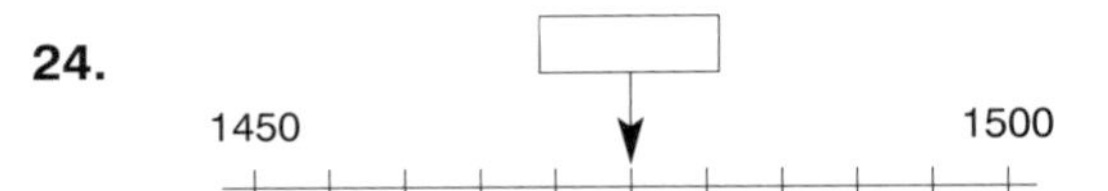

/5

Write **S** for **symmetrical** or **NS** for **not symmetrical** for each shape.

25. 26. 27. 28. 29. 30.

______ ______ ______ ______ ______ ______

/6

Answer these.

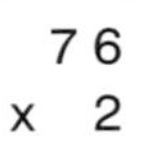

31. 76×2 = ______

32. 48×3 = ______

33. 29×5 = ______

34. 73×4 = ______

/4

Use a ruler to measure the sides of each rectangle.

Write the length, width and perimeter for these in centimetres.

35.

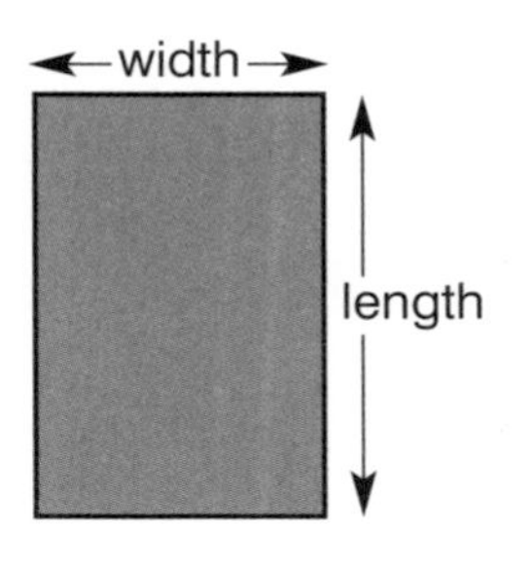

Length = ______cm

Width = ______cm

Perimeter = ______cm

36

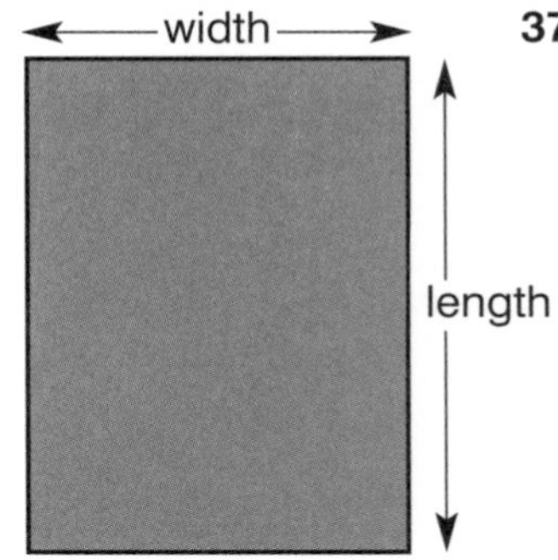

Length = ______cm

Width = ______cm

Perimeter = ______cm

37.

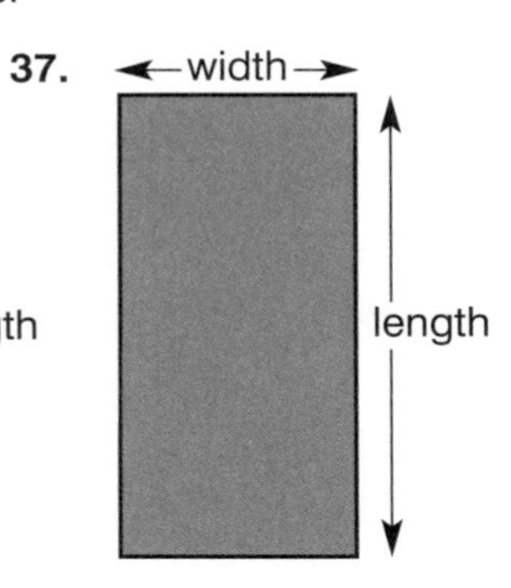

Length = ______cm

Width = ______cm

Perimeter = ______cm

38.

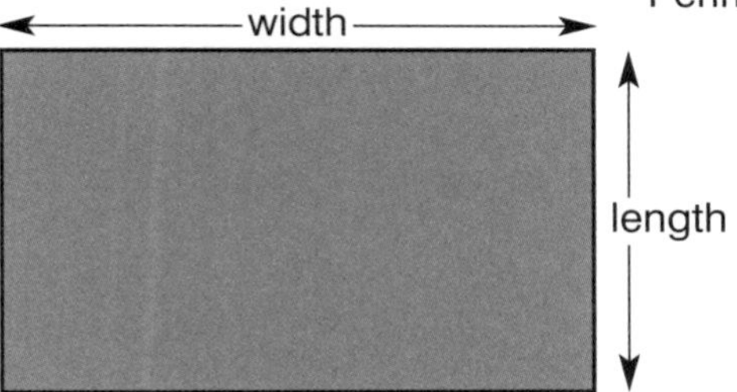

Length = ______cm

Width = ______cm

Perimeter = ______cm

/4

Read and answer these.

39. There are 245 children in Robert's school and 249 children in Julia's school. How many children are there in the two schools in total? ____________

40. Mr Allen bought 325ml of blue paint and 590ml of yellow paint. He mixed them together to make green paint. How much green paint did he have? ____________

/2

/40

PAPER 13

Complete these.

1. ☐ ÷ 3 = 7
2. 24 ÷ ☐ = 2
3. ☐ x 9 = 36
4. 30 ÷ 5 = ☐
5. 8 x ☐ = 64
6. ☐ x 7 = 28

/6

7. Which of these could be the missing number? Choose the correct answer.

   $3554 < \underline{\qquad\qquad}$

   a) 3468 **b)** 3099 **c)** 3604 **d)** 3509

/1

8. What is the rule for this sequence? Circle the correct answer.

   130 → 105 → 80 → 55 → 30

   a) – 35 **b)** – 25 **c)** + 25 **d)** – 15

/1

Write these decimals as fractions.

9. 20.6 ____________
10. 4.9 ____________
11. 0.8 ____________
12. 7.2 ____________
13. 16.5 ____________

/5

Answer these problems.

14. A brick weighs 2.5 kilograms. If a builder puts 40 bricks in his wheelbarrow, what is the total weight of the bricks? ____________

15. A bucket is filled with $3\frac{1}{2}$ litres of water. 500ml of water is poured out to make some cement. How many litres of water are left in the bucket? ____________

16. A decorator needs 25 litres of paint to paint a wall. He buys 4 tins of paint, each holding $5\frac{1}{2}$ litres of paint. How much more paint does he need? ____________

/3

Round these to the nearest 10.

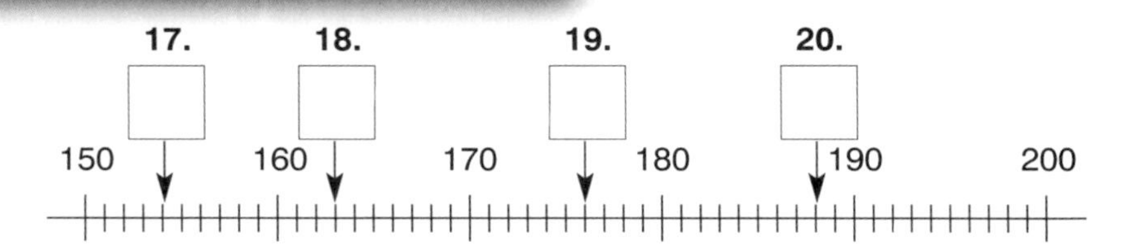

Look at the number machine. Copy and complete the table.

	21.	22.	23.	24.	25.	26.
IN	17		26		14	
OUT		47		52		61

/4

/6

Write these times.

27. 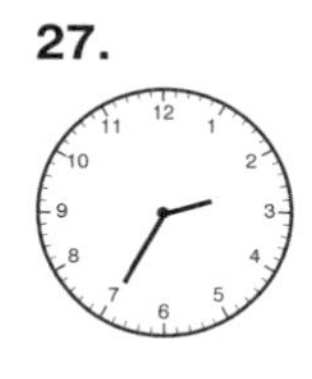

28. 

29. 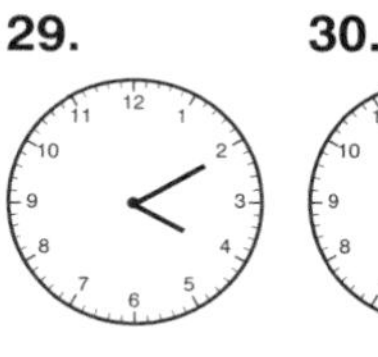

30. 

31.

32. 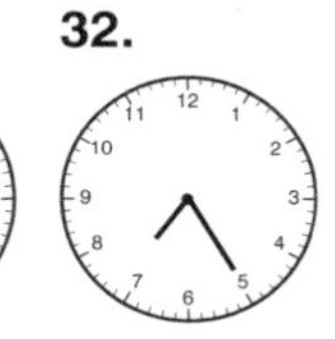

_______ _______ _______ _______ _______ _______

/6

Answer these.

33. How many 500ml bottles will fill a 1 litre jug? _______________

34. How many 100ml large spoons will fill a 1 litre jug? _______________

35. How many 250ml cups will fill a 1 litre jug? _______________

36. How many 5ml teaspoons will fill a 100ml large spoon? _______________

37. How many 500ml bottles will fill a 2 litre jug? _______________

38. How many 100ml large spoons will fill a 500ml water bottle? _______________

/6

What is the perimeter of each of these rooms?

39.

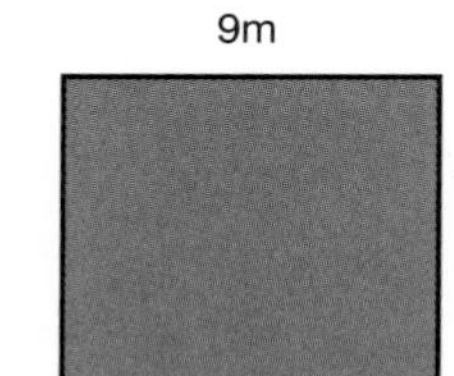

Perimeter = ________

40.

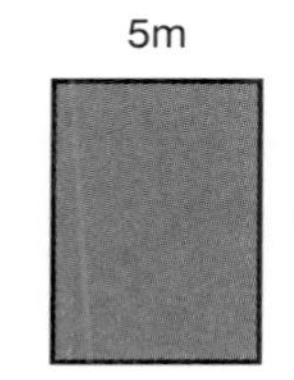

Perimeter = ________

/2

/40

PAPER 14

1. Complete this.

☐	x	☐	→	18
x		x		
6	x	☐	→	30
↓		↓		
12		45		

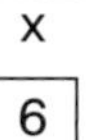

/1

2. In a shop, drinks cost £1.50 and chocolate bars cost 50p.
Daniel buys 3 drinks and some chocolate bars for his family
and he spends £7 altogether. How many chocolate bars does he buy? ________

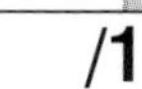

/1

Complete these.

3. $838 - 526 =$ ______

4. $662 - 349 =$ ______

5. $717 - 281 =$ ______

6. $834 - 472 =$ ______

7. $643 - 467 =$ ______

8. $502 - 136 =$ ______

/6

How many lines of symmetry are there for these shapes?

9. 

10. 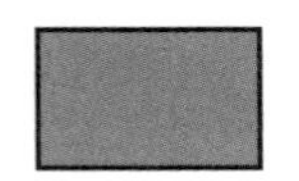

11. 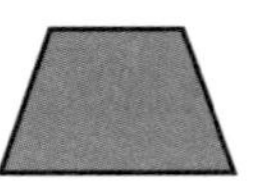

12. 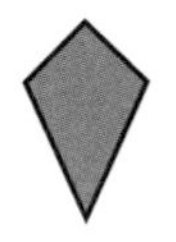

__________ __________ __________ __________ **/4**

13. Write the missing number. 7825 = 7000 + __________ + 20 + 5

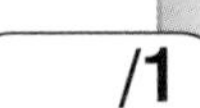

The digits 1 to 9 are missing from these additions.
Complete them with the digits in the correct place.

14.

```
   2 8 9
 + 6 □ 4
 -------
   □ 0 □
```

15.

```
   □ 0 □
 + 3 4 9
 -------
   9 □ 1
```

16.

```
   2 □ 4
 + □ 6 □
 -------
   7 5 1
```

/3

Write the number shown on each abacus.

17. 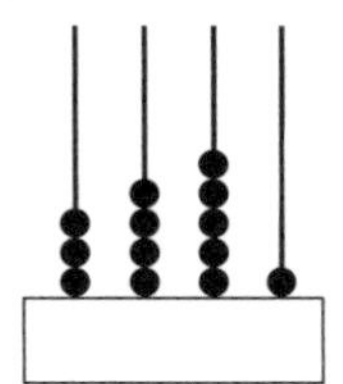

18. 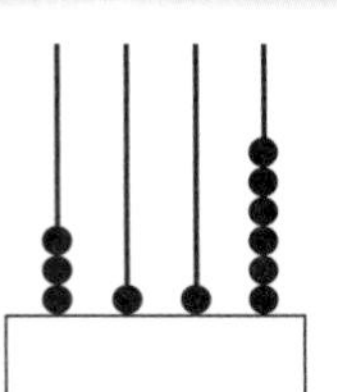

19. 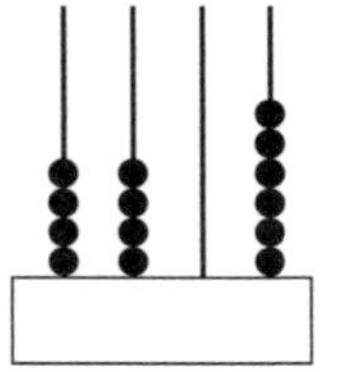

/3

20. A square has a perimeter of 36 centimetres. Circle the length of each side.

a) 6cm **b)** 9cm **c)** 8cm **d)** 12cm **/1**

21. A square has an area of 25 square centimetres. Circle the length of each side.

a) 3cm **b)** 10cm **c)** 6cm **d)** 5cm **/1**

Find the pattern for the sequence and write the missing numbers.

22. 7039 ____ 5039 ____ 3039 2039

23. ____ 625 630 635 ____ 645

24. 170 ____ 200 215 230 ____

25. 1650 1600 1550 ____ ____ 1400

26. ____ 1893 ____ 1693 1593 1493

/5

Three people each have **750** stickers to give away in a shopping centre. Complete this table, writing in the afternoon totals.

		Stickers given out		
		Morning	Afternoon	Total
27.	Ali	290		520
28.	Ben	310		690
29.	Claire	410		730

30. How many stickers did Ali have left at the end of the day? ____________

31. How many more did Claire give away than Ben? ____________

32. How many more did Ben give away in the afternoon than in the morning? ____________

33. How many stickers were left in total at the end of the day? ____________

/7

34. Circle the net that will **not** fold up to make a cube.

A
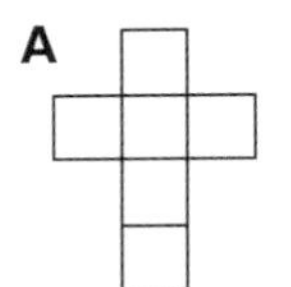

B
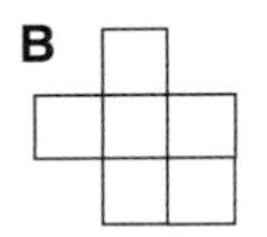

C
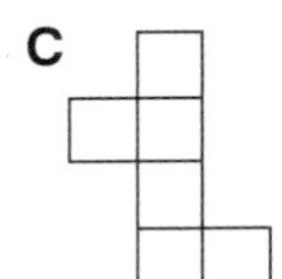

D
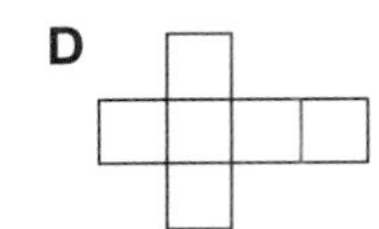

/1

Draw the weight of each bag on to the scales to the nearest $\frac{1}{2}$ kg.

35.

36.

37.

38.

/4

Which is the best buy in each pair? Tick your choice.

39. **A**

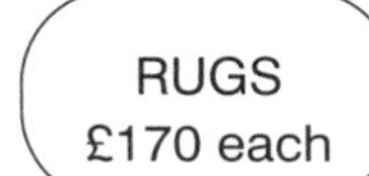

OR

B

2 RUGS
for £350

40. **A**

BED £500
Save £200
today!

OR

B

BED £500
Half-price
today!

/2

/40

PAPER 15

1. What number is the arrow pointing to? Circle the correct answer.

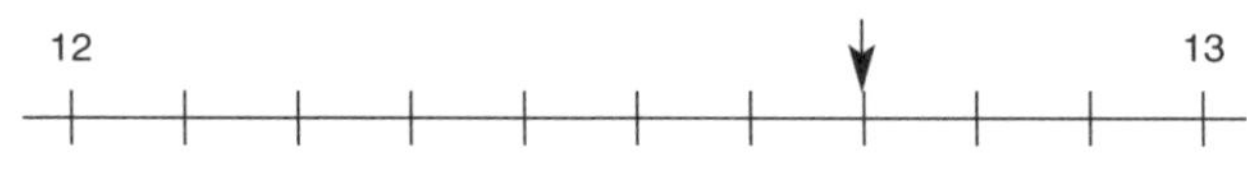

a) 12.7 **b)** 12.52 **c)** 12.6 **d)** 12.62

/1

Write the missing numbers.

2. 5486 = ______ + 400 + ______ + 6

3. 6945 = 6000 + ______ + ______ + 5

4. 8294 = ______ + ______ + 90 + 4

/3

Write the missing numbers in these sequences.

5. 1587	____	1607	1617	1627	____
6. 4602	____	4802	4902	____	5102
7. 3133	3123	____	____	2993	2983
8. ____	5155	5165	5175	5185	____
9. 1090	1075	____	1045	____	1015

/5

10. The sides of a square are 6cm. What is the area of this square? ________ /1

11. A builder buys some floor tiles of two different weights. He buys five 3kg tiles and some $2\frac{1}{2}$kg tiles. He weighs the whole load and it totals 35kg. How many $2\frac{1}{2}$kg tiles does he buy? ________ /1

12. The digits 1, 2 and 3 are missing from the addition. Write each digit in the correct place.

$$\begin{array}{r} \square\,7\,\square \\ +\ 6\,5\,8 \\ \hline 8\,\square\,0 \\ \hline \end{array}$$

/1

Look at the map showing the journey time of a bus. Work out the time the bus will be at each stop and complete this bus timetable.

	Bus Stop	Time
Start	A	10.05
13.	B	________
14.	C	________
15.	D	________
16.	E	________
17.	F	________
18.	A	________

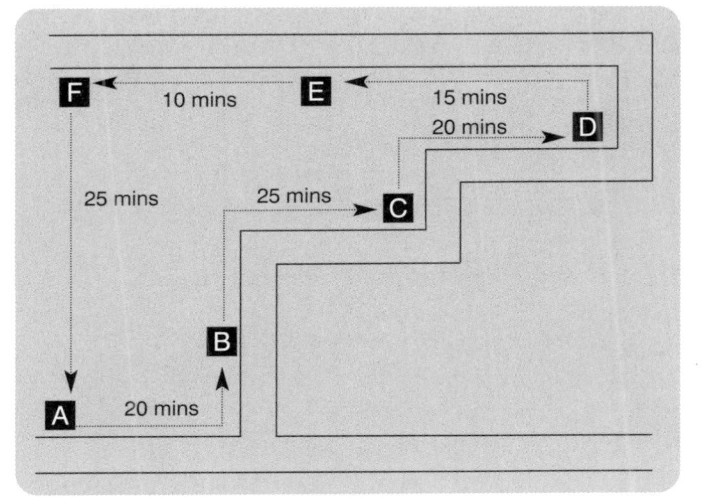

/6

Write <or > for each pair of lengths.

19. 6m 10cm ☐ 620cm

20. 480m ☐ 3km 800m

21. 3300cm ☐ 3m 13cm

22. 2km 212m ☐ 2120m

23. 508cm ☐ 5m

24. 9700m ☐ 9km 70m

/6

Complete these.

25. $\begin{array}{r} 618 \\ -\ 356 \\ \hline \end{array}$

26. $\begin{array}{r} 482 \\ -\ 247 \\ \hline \end{array}$

27. $\begin{array}{r} 714 \\ -\ 290 \\ \hline \end{array}$

28. $\begin{array}{r} 651 \\ -\ 182 \\ \hline \end{array}$

29. $\begin{array}{r} 942 \\ -\ 483 \\ \hline \end{array}$

30. $\begin{array}{r} 706 \\ -\ 428 \\ \hline \end{array}$

/6

31. What number does 485 round to, to the nearest 10? Circle the correct answer.

a) 500 **b)** 480 **c)** 490 **d)** 510

/1

This bar graph shows the average lifespan of some animals.

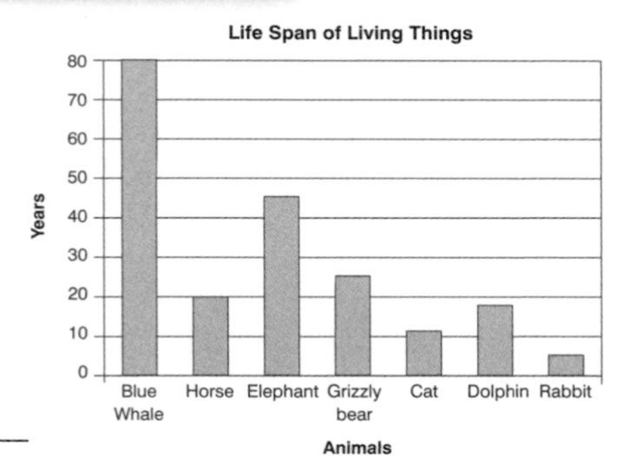

32. What has a life span of 45 years? ____________

33. What has the longest life span? ____________

34. What has the shortest life span? ____________

35. What is the lifespan of a grizzly bear? ____________

36. What has a life span of about 12 years? ____________

37. How much longer is a blue whale expected to live than an elephant? ____________

38. What is expected to live six years more than a cat? ____________

/7

What is the perimeter of each of these rectangles?

39. 8m

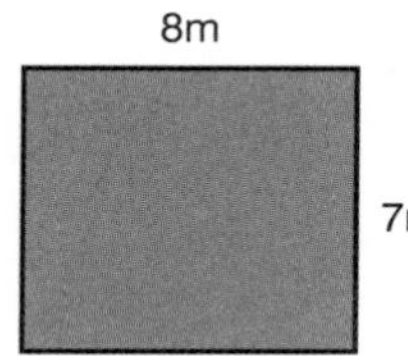

7m

Perimeter = ________

40. 14m

5m

Perimeter = ________

/2

/40

PAPER 16

Complete this table.

	Length in m and cm	Length in cm
1.	____m ____cm	922cm
2.	1m 50cm	____cm
3.	____m ____cm	280cm
4.	3m 25cm	____cm
5.	____m ____cm	705cm
6.	6m 9cm	____cm

/6

Answer these time problems.

7. A TV programme starts at 7.15pm and lasts for 35 minutes. What time will it end?

____

8. Nathan gets up at 7.40am and leaves for school 45 minutes later.
What time does he leave for school? ________

9. A cake takes 55 minutes to bake. It was put in the oven at 4.35pm.
When will it be ready? ______________

10. Sophie is playing at the park and it is 11.50am. She has to leave for home at 12.30pm. How much longer does she have left to play? ______________

/4

11. What is the name of this shape? Circle the correct answer.

a) cylinder **b)** cuboid

c) prism **d)** pyramid

/1

12. How much water is in this jug?

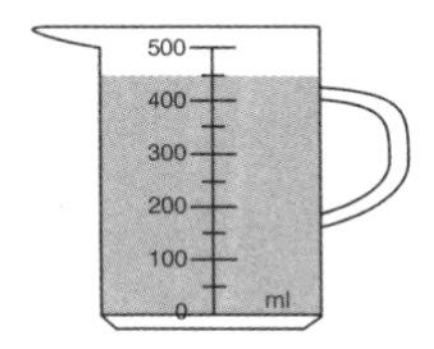

______________ ml

/1

Write the number shown on each abacus.

13.

14. 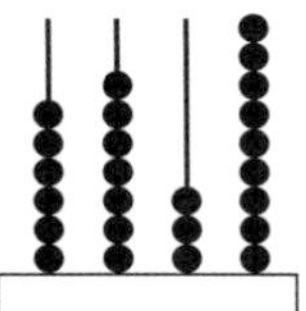

15. 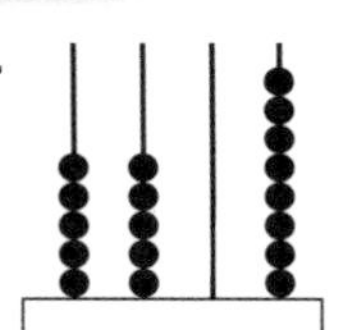

16. 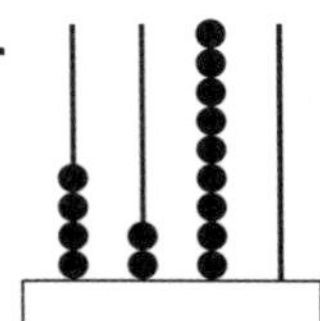

/4

Two numbers in each sequence have been swapped over. Circle the two numbers.

17. 953 955 957 951 949 947 945

18. 1005 975 985 995 965 955 945

19. 420 620 1220 1020 820 1420 1620

/3

Write < or > to make each statement true.

20. 7149 ☐ 7145 **21.** 3433 ☐ 3622 **22.** 4608 ☐ 6408

23. 9327 ☐ 9317 **24.** 8001 ☐ 7995 **25.** 6746 ☐ 6647

/6

These should show a line of symmetry. Write True or False beside each shape.

26.	27.	28.	29.	30.
	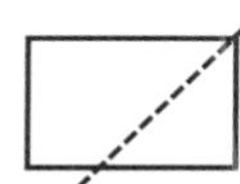	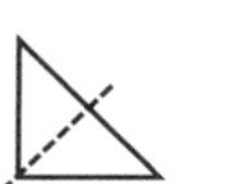	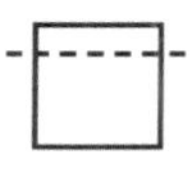	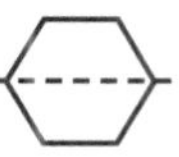
_______	_______	_______	_______	_______

/5

Complete these.

31. ______ ÷8 = 7 **32.** 24 ÷ ______ = 3 **33.** ______ x 7 = 28

34. 60 ÷ 5 = ______ **35.** 6 x ______ = 42 **36.** ______ x 4 = 36

37. 54÷ ______ = 9 **38.** 8 x ______ = 48

/8

39. What is the difference between 148 and 215? ____________

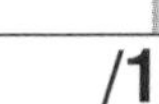

/1

40. Look at these coins. Circle all of the amounts you can make exactly by using any 3 of these coins at a time.

70p 42p £1.05 55p 35p

/1

/40

PAPER 17

Answer these.

1. What is 27 added to 34? ______ **2.** What is 56 more than 128? ______

3. What is the total of 48 and 26? ______ **4.** What is 74 added to 84? ______

/4

5. Complete this.

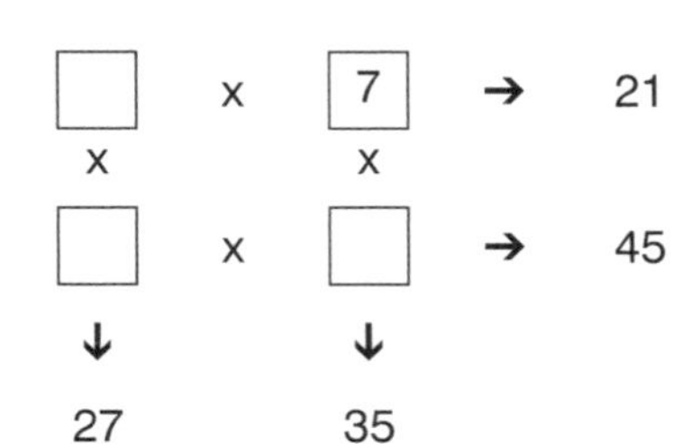

6. What is the weight of this parcel?

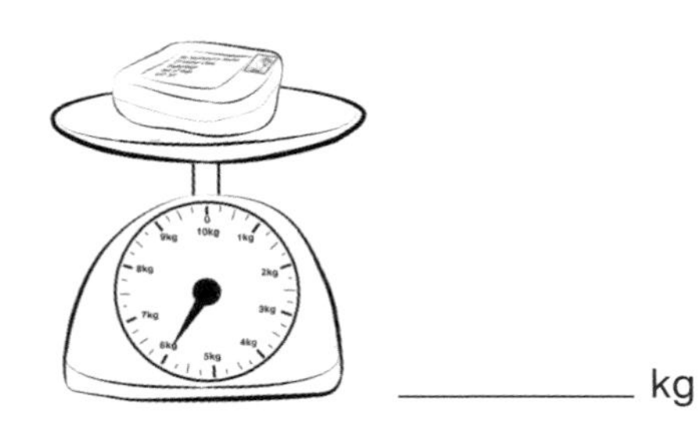

_______ kg

/2

Write these times.

7. 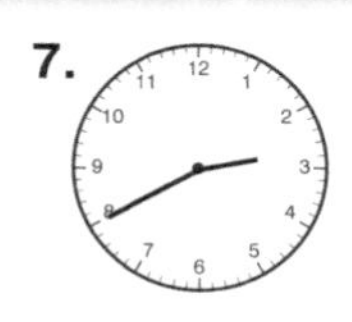

8. 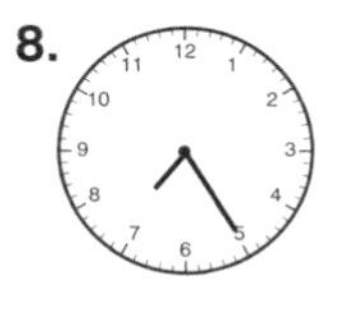

9. 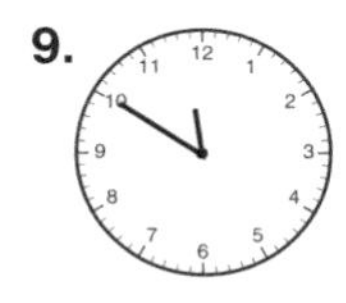

10. 

/4

Look at the position of each arrow. Round to the nearest 100.

11. **12.** **13.** **14.**

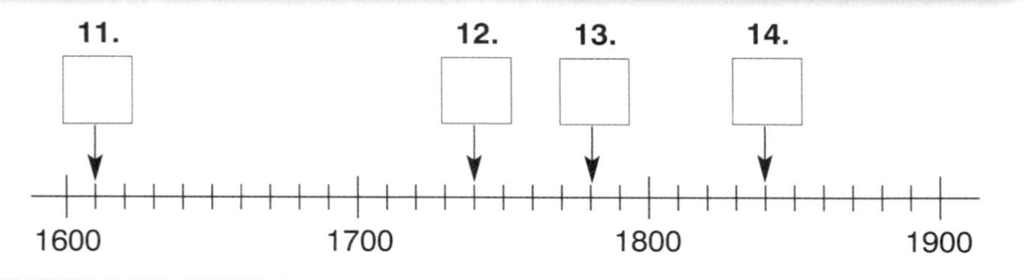

/4

Complete the table.

	15.	16.	17.	18.	19.	20.
IN	34		45		56	
OUT		12		8		23

/6

Write each group of numbers in order starting with the smallest.

21. 7692 7052 7162 7962 ________________

22. 6900 5200 5800 6100 ________________

23. 9407 9470 9417 9371 ________

24. 8804 8840 8880 8408 ________

/4

25. What is the remainder when 183 is divided by 10? Circle the correct answer.

a) 8 **b)** 3 **c)** 9 **d)** 7

/1

Answer these additions.

26.	**27.**	**28.**	**29.**
752	307	273	486
+ 196	+ 589	+ 179	+ 315
____	____	____	____

/4

Answer these subtractions.

30.	**31.**	**32.**	**33.**
927	742	406	853
− 556	− 249	− 287	− 576
____	____	____	____

/4

Read and answer these.

34. A bus holds 56 passengers. How many people will 4 buses hold? ________

35. Mr Benson travels 26km each day to and from work.
He works 5 days a week. How far does he travel altogether in a week? ________

36. A market stall has 6 crates of melons.
There are 48 melons in a crate. How many melons are there in total? ________

37. A farmer fills 5 trays of eggs.
Each tray holds 36 eggs. How many eggs does the farmer have? ________

38. The battery in a mobile phone lasts for 6 days. How many hours does the battery last? ________

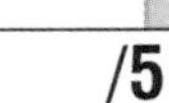

/5

39. The temperature in Leeds is 5°C. New York is 8 degrees colder than Leeds.
Circle the temperature in New York.

a) −13°C **b)** −2°C **c)** 3°C **d)** −3°C

/1

40. Draw an arrow on this line to show $2\frac{3}{4}$.

0 1 2 3 4

/1

/40

PAPER 18

1. Circle the two shapes that have $\frac{2}{3}$ shaded.

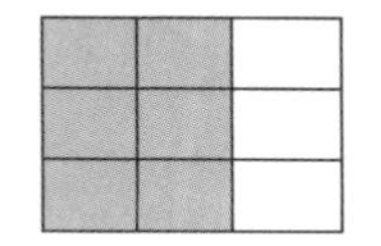
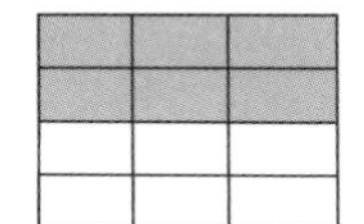
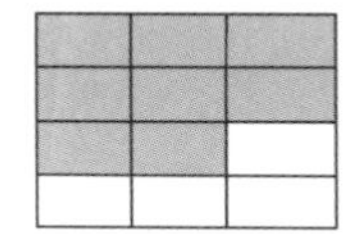
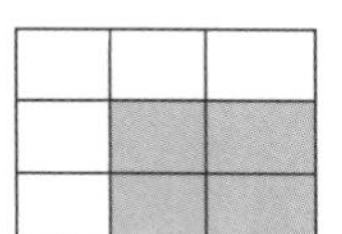
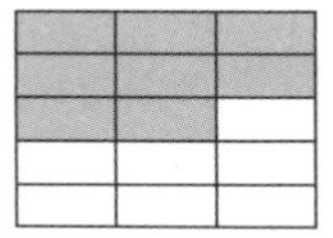

/1

2. Circle three numbers that add to total 170.

45 85 30 60 55

/1

Write the next two numbers in each sequence.

3. 9134 9114 9094 9074 9054 ______ ______

4. 1578 1580 1582 1584 1586 ______ ______

5. 8206 7206 6206 5206 4206 ______ ______

6. 6530 6525 6520 6515 6510 ______ ______

/4

Write each group of numbers in order, starting with the smallest.

7. 2391 8431 5076 3928 ______

8. 5993 4032 9042 9053 ______

9. 5072 4021 3506 5070 ______

10. 9138 9813 3189 8931 ______

/4

11. What is the name of this shape? Circle the correct answer.

a) quadrilateral **b)** pentagon

c) hexagon **d)** heptagon

/1

12. A rectangle has a perimeter of 48cm. The shorter sides are 8cm in length.

What is the length of the longer sides? ____________

/1

A group of children were sorted into these sets. Complete the table for the group.

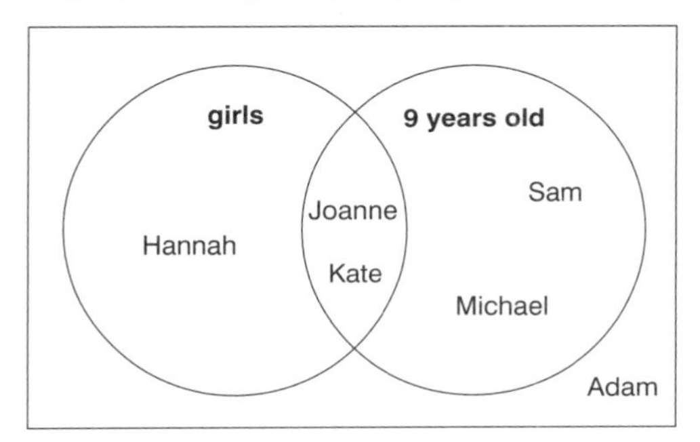

Boys	
Name	Age
Michael	9
13.	8
14.	9

Girls	
Name	Age
Kate	15.
16.	9
17.	8

/5

Write the numbers at each arrow.

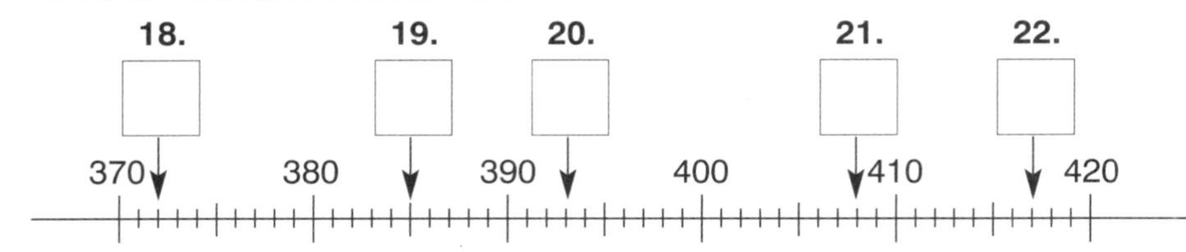

/5

23. There are 24 balls in a box. $\frac{1}{3}$ of them are blue, $\frac{1}{6}$ of them are red and the rest of them are yellow. How many of the balls are yellow? ____________

/1

Answer these.

24. 56 x 2 = _____ **25.** 43 x 3 = _____ **26.** 18 x 6 = _____ **27.** 23 x 7 = _____

/4

Complete this chart to show the start and finish positions for each turn.

Start position	Turn	End position
28. A	$\frac{1}{4}$ turn clockwise	
29. D	$\frac{1}{2}$ turn anticlockwise	
30. C	$\frac{1}{4}$ turn clockwise	
31. B	$\frac{1}{4}$ turn anticlockwise	
32. A	$\frac{1}{2}$ turn clockwise	

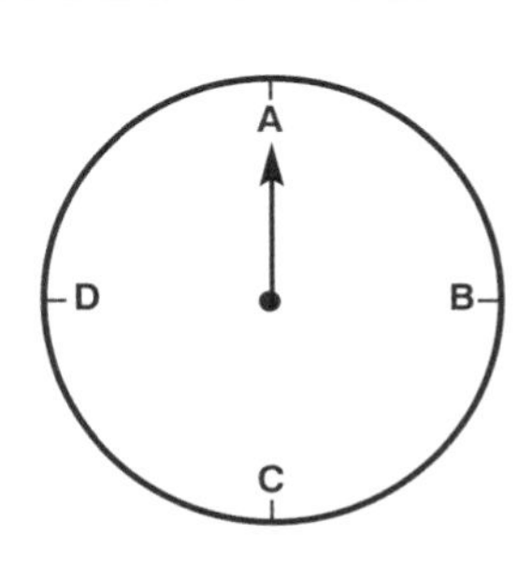

/5

What is the perimeter and area of each of these rectangles?

7cm
11cm

33. Perimeter = ______cm

34. Area = ______cm²

12m
9m

35. Perimeter = ______cm

36. Area = ______cm²

/4

Look at the sign for these theatre tickets and work out the least expensive ways for these families to buy the tickets. Write the total costs for each family.

Letts' Theatre
Family Ticket £70
(2 adults + up to 4 children)
Adult Ticket £28
Child Ticket £12

37. Two adults and two children = ____________

38. One adult and three children = ____________

39. Two adults and one child = ____________

/3

40. How many edges has a cube got? Circle the correct answer.

a) 8 **b)** 6 **c)** 12 **d)** 10

/1

/40

PAPER 19

Write the halfway numbers for each of these number lines.

1.

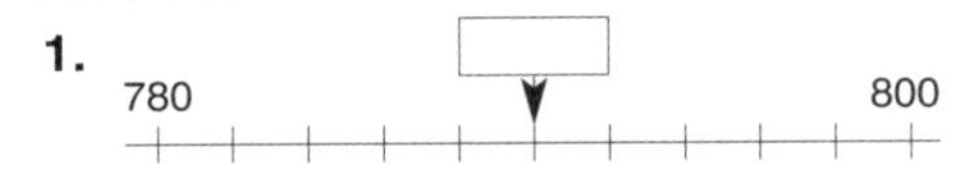

2.

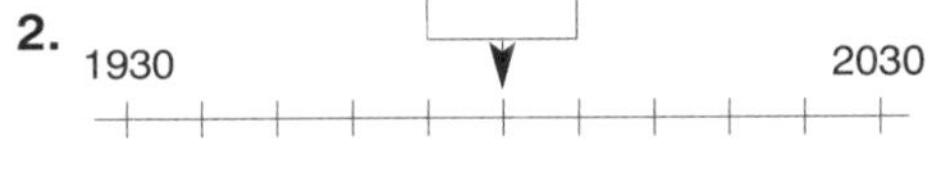

3. 570 ____ 670

4. 3450 ____ 3500

5. 2000 ____ 2100

6.

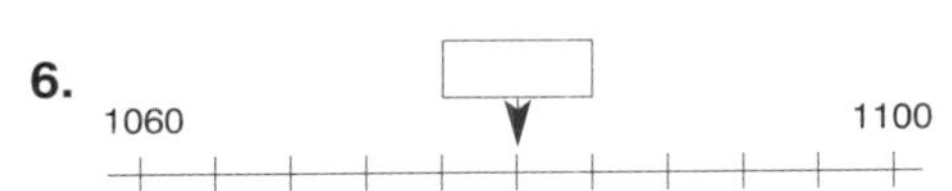

/6

Write these times.

7.

8.

9.

10.

__________ __________ __________ __________

/4

11. What is $7\frac{3}{10}$ as a decimal? Circle the correct answer.

a) 7.1 **b)** 7.3 **c)** 7.13 **d)** 7.33

/1

Read and answer these.

12. A man spends £140 on petrol for his car every week.
How much will he spend in total over 4 weeks? __________

13. Mrs Jones' train fare costs £60 a day. She takes the train for 6 days.
What will be the total cost? __________

14. A boat can be hired for £28 for half an hour.
How much would it cost for $1\frac{1}{2}$ hours? __________

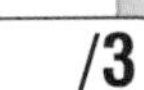

/3

Complete these, writing in the correct signs, = < or >.

15. 5 x 7 ☐ 35 **16.** 35 ÷ 7 ☐ 6 **17.** 8 x 4 ☐ 36 **18.** 32 ÷ 4 ☐ 7

/4

Write the amount of water in each of these.

19. 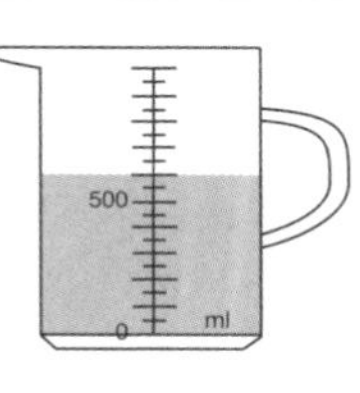

20. 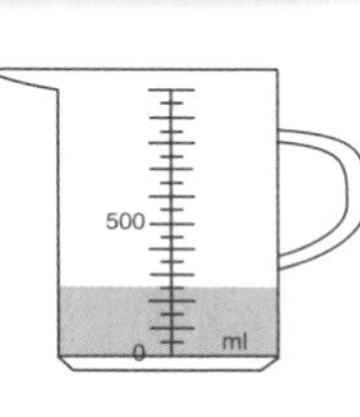

21. 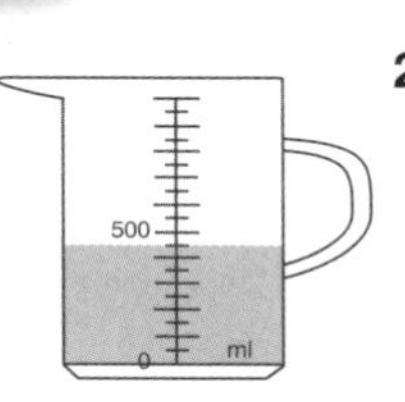

22. 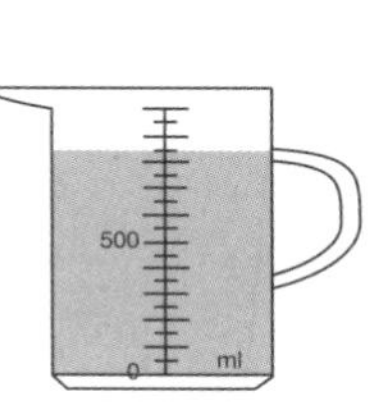

______ ______ ______ ______

/4

What is the area of each shape?

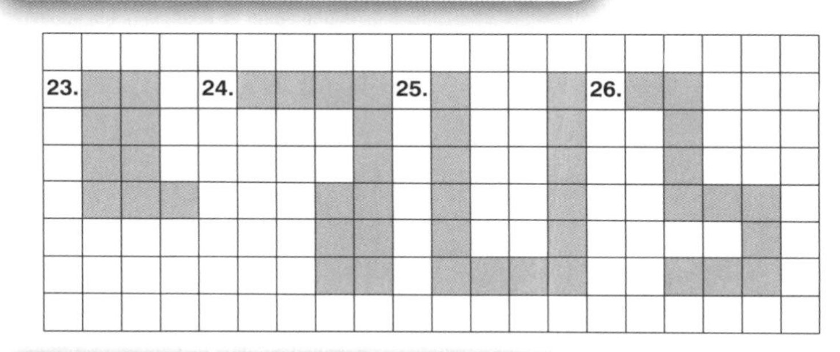

23. ______ squares

24. ______ squares

25. ______ squares

26. ______ squares

/4

Round these to the nearest 10.

27. 28. 29. 30.

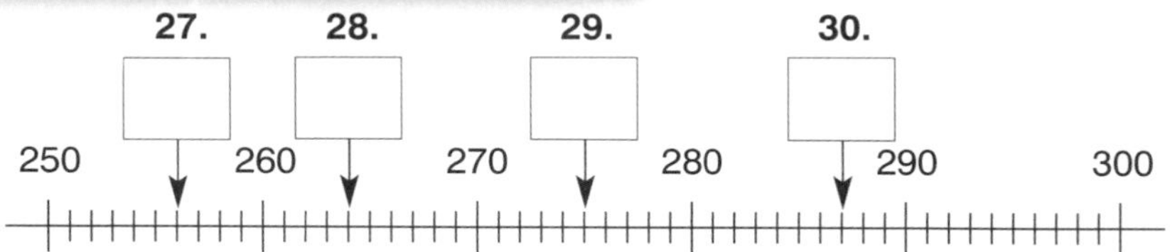

/4

Complete this chart.

	Length in km and m	Length in m
31.	8km 700m	______m
32.	6km 135m	______m
33.	______km ______m	4650m

	Length in km and m	Length in m
34.	10km 8m	______m
35.	4km 50m	______m
36.	______km ______m	9045m

/6

Write the number of lines of symmetry on these shapes.

37.

______

38.

______

39.

______

40.

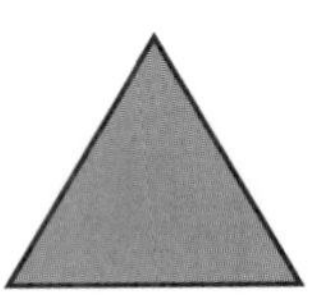

______

/4

/40

PAPER 20

Write the number at each arrow.

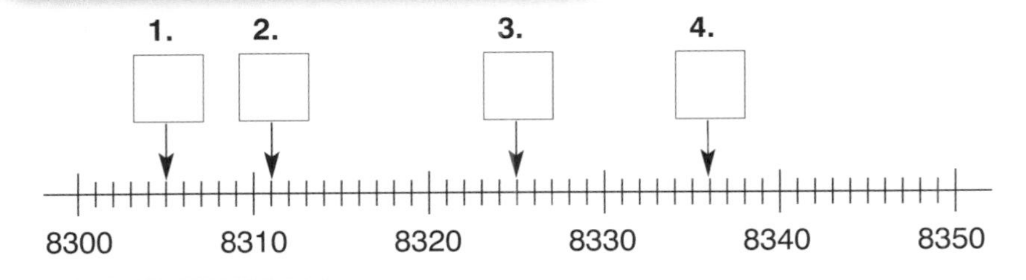

/4

Complete these.

5. 3 weeks = ______ days

6. 120 minutes = ______ hours

7. 4 hours = ______ minutes

8. 70 days = ______ weeks

9. 5 years = ______ months

10. 240 hours = ______ days

/6

11. Complete this multiplication grid.

X	7	3	8
9			72
4	28		32
5		15	

/1

12. George has £33 to spend on some drinks and some cakes.
The drinks cost £2 each and the cakes cost £5 each.
How many drinks and cakes could he buy for exactly £33? ______________

/1

For each shape write the number of acute, obtuse and right angles.

13. 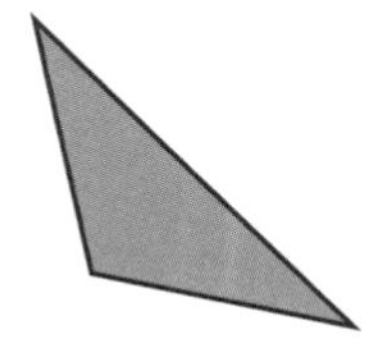

_____ acute angles
_____ obtuse angles
_____ right angles

14. 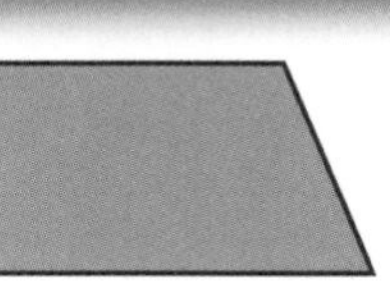

_____ acute angles
_____ obtuse angles
_____ right angles

15. 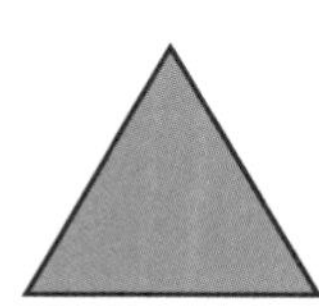

_____ acute angles
_____ obtuse angles
_____ right angles

16. 

_____ acute angles
_____ obtuse angles
_____ right angles

/4

Shade one more square on each of these to make them into nets of closed cubes.

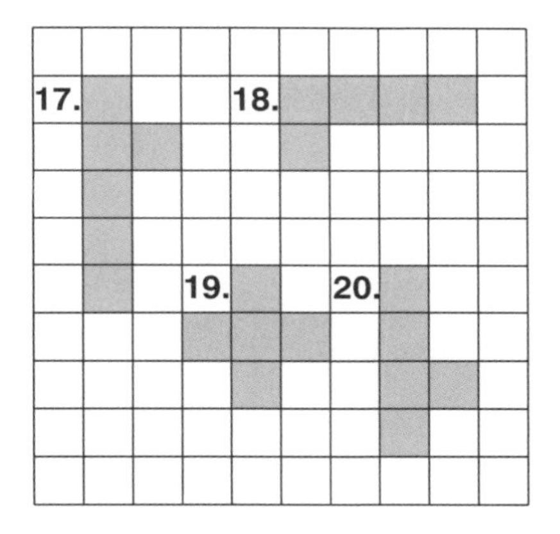

/4

This is a 'subtract 12' machine. Write the numbers that enter the machine.

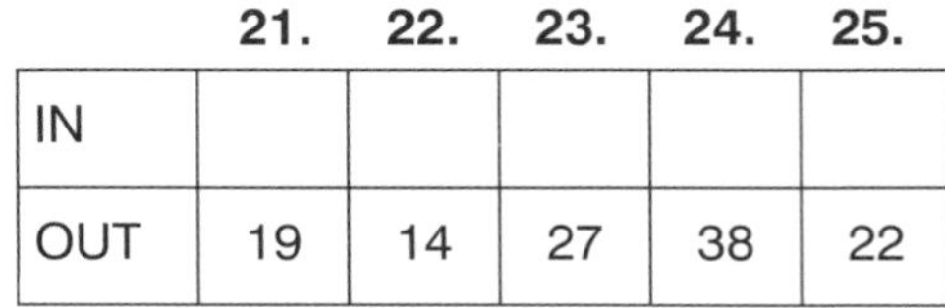

	21.	22.	23.	24.	25.
IN					
OUT	19	14	27	38	22

/5

Work out the mystery number for each of these.

26. When I divide my number by 7 the answer is 6. ______________

27. When I multiply my number by 4 the answer is 36. ______________

28. When I double my number and then add 3 the answer is 25. ______________

/3

Write each of the missing digits 0–9 to complete these calculations.

0 1 2 3 4 5 6 7 8 9

29. ☐ ☐ + 1 4 = 4 2

30. 2 7 + ☐ ☐ = 4 3

31. 5 x ☐ = 4 5

32. 8 x ☐ = 2 4

33. ☐ ☐ - 2 5 = 4 5

34. 8 6 - ☐ ☐ = 3 2

/6

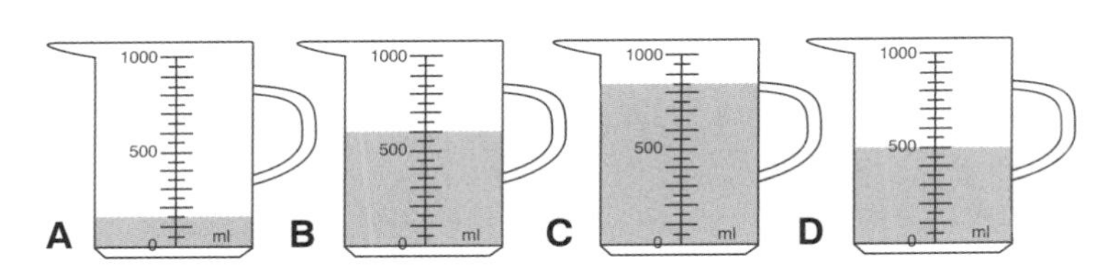

35. Which two jugs total exactly 1 litre? ______________

36. Which jug is 100ml less than B? ______________

37. Which two jugs total 1l 100ml? ______________

38. Which two jugs have a difference of 450ml? ______________

/4

Measure the length of each side of these rectangles.

What is the perimeter of each shape?

39.

Perimeter = ______cm

40.

Perimeter = ______cm

/2

/40

PAPER 21

1. Write the missing digit so that this 2-digit number is a multiple of 6.

2. Which of these is a symmetrical shape? Tick the correct shape.

a)  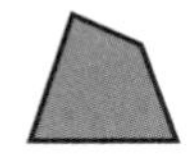

b) 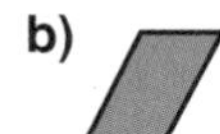

c) 

d)  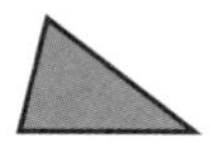

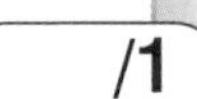

Complete these.

3. ☐ x 8 = 32

4. 55 ÷ 5 = ☐

5. 6 x ☐ = 42

6. ☐ x 3 = 24

7. ☐ ÷6 = 6

8. 27 ÷ ☐ = 9

Which is the best buy in each pair? Circle your choice.

9. A Dining Table £113 SALE £40 off OR B Dining Table £130 SALE £50 off

10. A 4 dining chairs £360 OR B 6 dining chairs £480

/2

11. Each sack of sugar weighs 12kg.
How much does each box of rice weigh?

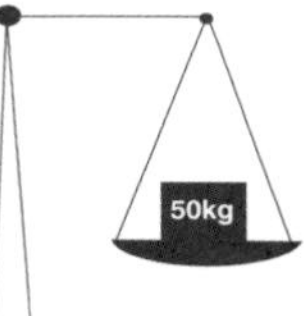

Box of rice = ______kg

/1

Write these times.

12. 

13. 

14. 

15. 

__________ __________ __________ __________

/4

Round these to the nearest 100.

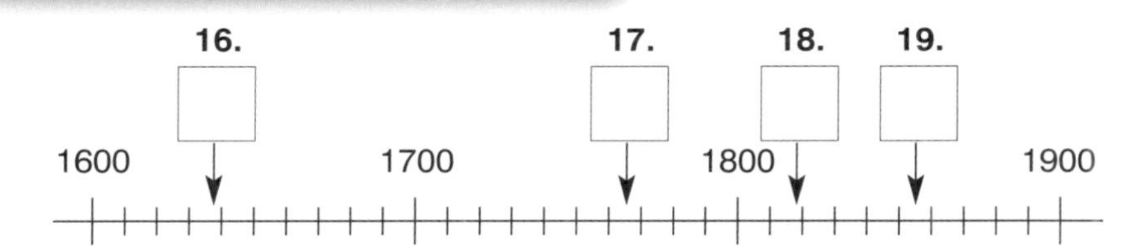

/4

20. Which of these could be the missing number? Write in the correct answer. 9454 > ______

a) 9445 **b)** 9544 **c)** 9455 **d)** 9504

/1

21. Circle all the multiples of 3 in this list of numbers. 46 32 42 27 38 45

/1

22. What fraction of this square is shaded?

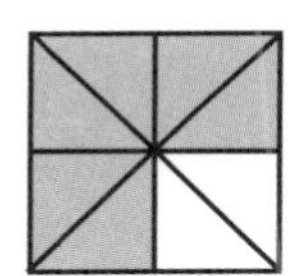

____

/1

Tick to show whether each angle is acute, obtuse or right-angled.

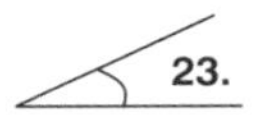

27.

28.

Angle	23.	24.	25.	26.	27.	28.
Acute						
Obtuse						
Right-angled						

/6

Answer these.

29. 18×3 = ______

30. 36×4 = ______

31. 25×8 = ______

32. 46×5 = ______

/4

Answer these.

33. $5\overline{)65}$ **34.** $4\overline{)64}$ **35.** $3\overline{)45}$ **36.** $2\overline{)46}$ /4

37. Draw a rectangle with an area of 14 squares.

38. What is the perimeter of this rectangle? ________ squares.

37. Draw a rectangle with an area of 18 squares.

38. What is the perimeter of this rectangle? ________ squares.

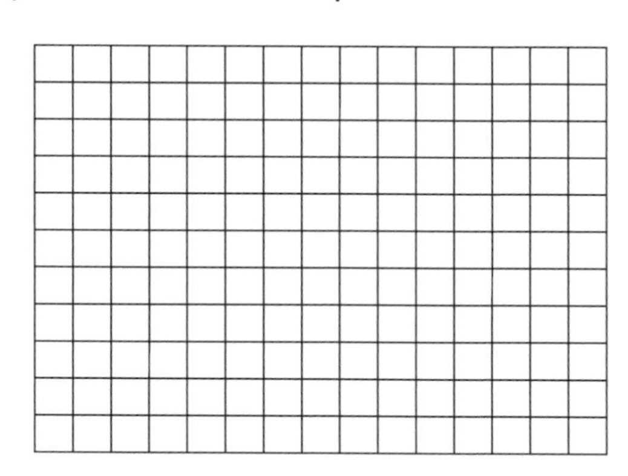

/4

/40

PAPER 22

Circle the fraction in each set that is not equivalent to the others.

1. $\frac{10}{20}$ $\frac{8}{16}$ $\frac{9}{24}$ $\frac{2}{4}$ **2.** $\frac{3}{12}$ $\frac{1}{4}$ $\frac{6}{24}$ $\frac{4}{18}$ **3.** $\frac{3}{9}$ $\frac{4}{12}$ $\frac{6}{16}$ $\frac{2}{6}$

/3

Complete the chart by rounding to the nearest 10 and 100.

	Round to nearest 10	Round to nearest 100
2198 →	**4.**	**5.**
4651 →	**6.**	**7.**
6327 →	**8.**	**9.**
5615 →	**10.**	**11.**

/8

12. What length is 8km 80m in metres? Circle the correct answer.

a) 8800m **b)** 880m **c)** 8080m **d)** 80080m

/1

Write the number shown on each abacus.

13. 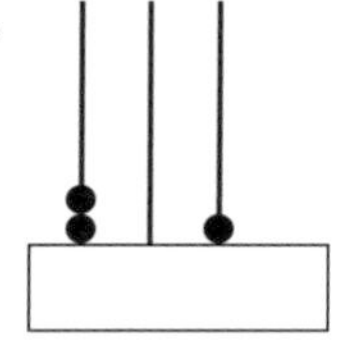

14. 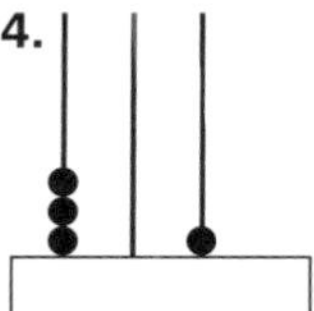

15. 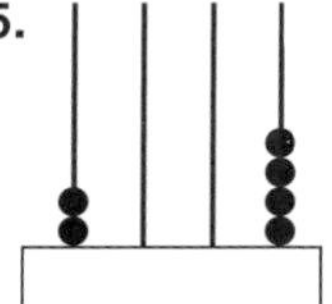

16. 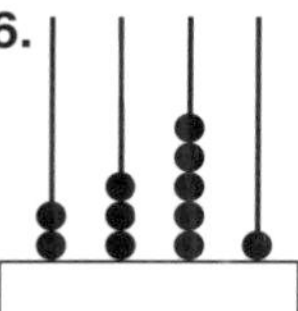

17. 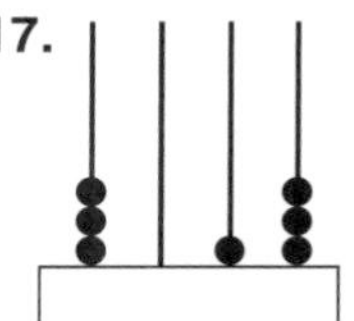

/5

18. How many sides has a heptagon got? Circle the correct answer.

a) 6 **b)** 5 **c)** 7 **d)** 8

/1

Complete these additions.

19. 852 + 649 = ______

20. 709 + 472 = ______

21. 638 + 836 = ______

22. 972 + 568 = ______

/4

23. James bought 3 drinks costing £1.20 each and 4 cakes costing 90p each. How much did he spend in total? ______________

/1

These nets will fold to make 3D shapes.
Match each net to the name of its shape.

24. 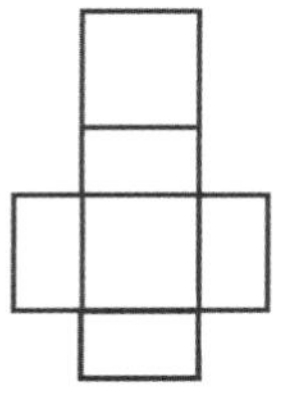

25. 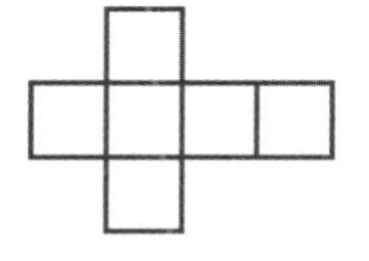

26. 

27. 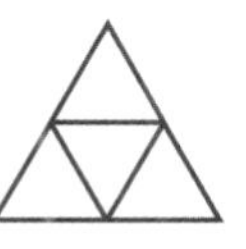

tetrahedron cuboid square based pyramid cube

/4

Draw each shape on the diagram.

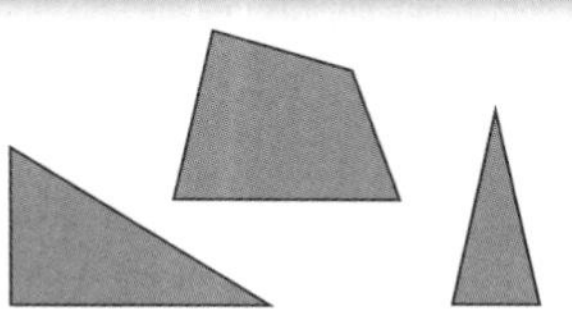

	Symmetrical	Not symmetrical
Some right angles	28.	29.
No right angles	30.	31.

/4

Circle the smallest number and underline the largest number in each group.

32. 802 810 811 809 **33.** 756 765 755 766

34. 490 488 486 480

/3

Calculate the area and perimeter of each of these rectangles.

35. area = ________

36. perimeter = ________

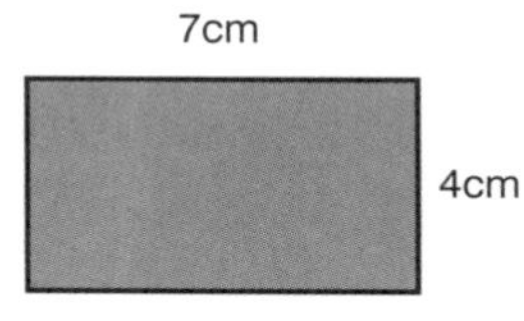

37. area = ________

38. perimeter = ________

39. area = ________

40. perimeter = ________

/6

/40

PAPER 23

1. The rule for this number sequence is double and then add 1.

Write the next number in the sequence. 1 3 7 15 ______

/1

Answer these.

2. 854 − 681 = ______

3. 803 − 295 = ______

4. 726 − 449 = ______

5. 624 − 387 = ______

/4

Write the numbers that enter this doubling machine.

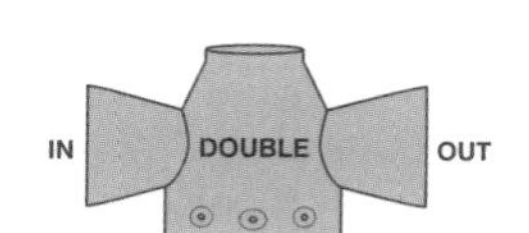

	6.	7.	8.	9.	10.
IN					
OUT	64	38	56	42	52

/5

Measure the shortest and longest sides of this shape. Measure them to the nearest half-centimetre.

11. Shortest side is ______ cm

12. Longest side is ______cm

/2

Work out the mystery number for each of these.

13. When I half my number and then add 1 the answer is 7. ____________

14. When I double my number and then subtract 2 the answer is 14. ____________

15. When I half my number and then subtract 3 the answer is 2. ____________

16. When I double my number and then add 5 the answer is 17. ____________

/4

Write the missing numbers in these sequences.

17. 140 155 ____ ____ 200 ____ 230

18. 208 ____ 204 202 ____ ____ 196

19. 325 ____ ____ ____ 345 350 355

20. 200 ____ ____ 290 320 ____ 380

/4

21. How many lines of symmetry does this shape have? Circle the correct answer.

a) 1 **b)** 6

c) 3 **d)** 2

/1

22. A boat costs £40 an hour to hire and then £8 each 10 minutes over the hour. How much would it cost in total if you had the boat for 1 hour and 20 minutes?

____

/1

Answer these.

23. What is 87 added to 36? ________

24. What is 62 more than 75? ________

25. What is the total of 58 and 26? ________

26. What is 74 added to 83? ________

/4

27. How many vertices does a cuboid have? Circle the correct answer.

a) 4 **b)** 8

c) 12 **d)** 6

28. Jamie weighs out 650 grams of pasta. Draw an arrow on the scale to show 650g.

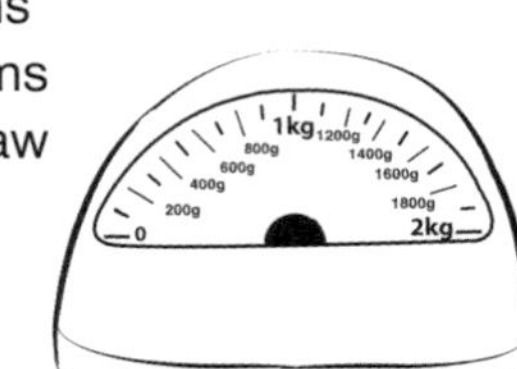

/2

The digits 3 and 4 are missing from these. Complete them.

29.

  8 9 □
− □ 5 2
  5 □ 2

30.

  8 □ 9
− □ 2 6
  5 2 □

31.

  5 8 □
− □ □ 1
  1 5 2

/3

Name the type of triangles shown in each set.

32. 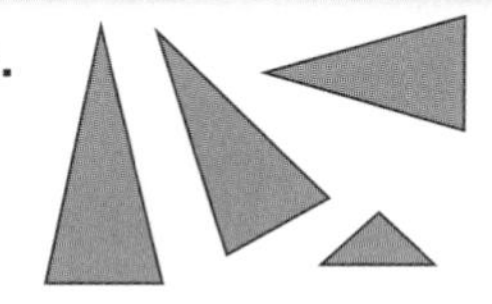 ____________

33. 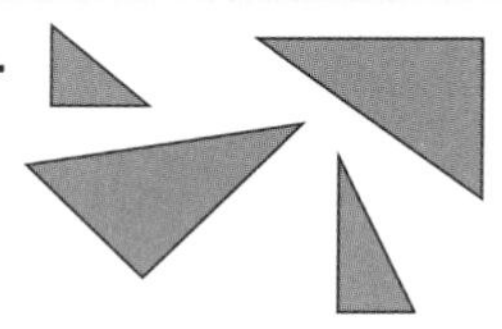 ____________

34. 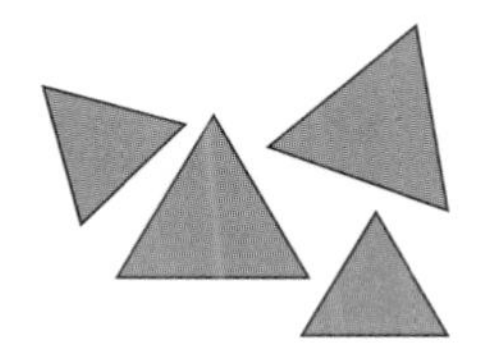 ____________

/3

This pictogram shows the number of shirts sold from a shop each day for a week.

Monday	👕👕👕
Tuesday	👕👕👕👕👕👕👕👕
Wednesday	👕👕👕👕👕👕
Thursday	👕👕👕👕
Friday	👕👕👕👕👕👕👕👕
Saturday	👕👕👕👕👕👕👕👕👕👕👕
Sunday	👕👕

👕 = 5 shirts

35. How many shirts were sold in total on Tuesday? ____________

36. On which day were 20 shirts sold? ____________

37. How many more shirts were sold on Wednesday than on Monday? ____________

38. How many shirts were sold altogether on Saturday and Sunday? ____________

/4

Write the number that is one more than each of these.

39. 1009 ____________

40. 1109 ____________

/2

/40

PAPER 24

Answer these.

1. $\square \div 3 = 9$ 2. $\square \div 2 = 14$ 3. $\square \div 5 = 5$ 4. $\square \div 4 = 12$ /4

5. Write the missing number to make this correct. $\frac{1}{4}$ of 12 = $\frac{1}{2}$ of $\square$ /1

Complete this chart to show the direction you would be facing after each turn.

	Start position, facing:	Turn	End position, now facing:
6.	north	$\frac{1}{4}$ turn anticlockwise	
7.	south	$\frac{1}{4}$ turn clockwise	
8.	west	$\frac{1}{4}$ turn anticlockwise	
9.	east	$\frac{1}{4}$ turn clockwise	

/4

10. What is 8.4 written as a fraction? Circle the correct answer.

a) $8\frac{1}{2}$ **b)** $8\frac{1}{10}$ **c)** $8\frac{2}{5}$ **d)** $8\frac{4}{5}$ /1

Write the next two numbers in each sequence.

11. 3450 3500 3550 3600 3650 ____ ____

12. 6520 6510 6500 6490 6480 ____ ____

13. 2050 2025 2000 1975 1950 ____ ____

14. 1159 1162 1165 1168 1171 ____ ____ /4

Write < or > to make these true.

15. 94.9 $\square$ 94.15 **16.** 14.23 $\square$ 16.2 **17.** 6.08 $\square$ 6.8 **18.** 32.7 $\square$ 34.81 /4

Answer these.

19. 834 − 556 = ______

20. 782 − 389 = ______

21. 467 − 249 = ______

22. 804 − 179 = ______

/4

Write the amount of water in each of these.

23.
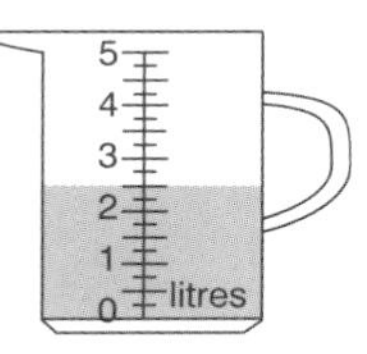

24.
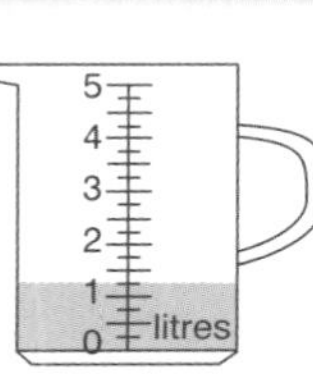

25.

26.
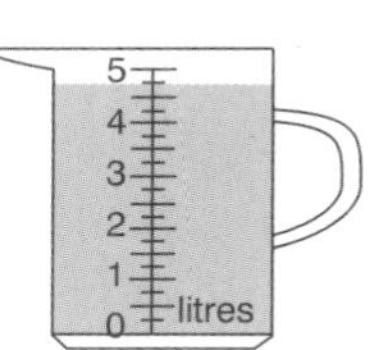

______ ______ ______ ______

/4

Write the numbers shown on each abacus.

27.
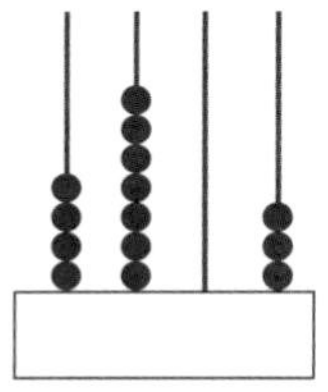

28.
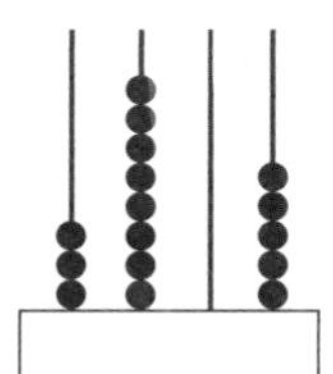

29.
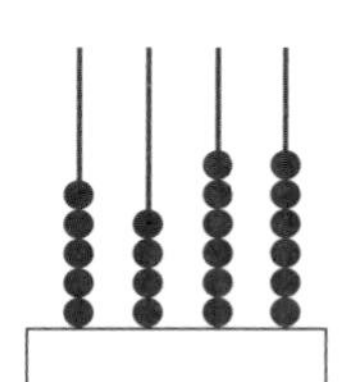

/3

Write the times shown on these clocks.

30.

31.

32.

33.

______ ______ ______ ______

34. Which number rounds to 1470 to the nearest 10? Circle the correct answer.

a) 1476 **b)** 1466 **c)** 1464 **d)** 1570

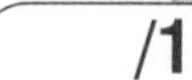

Write the number of faces for each of these shapes.

35.

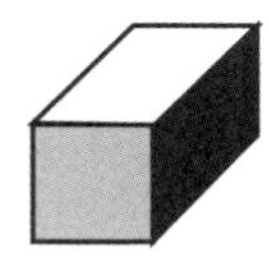

_____ square faces

_____ rectangle faces

35.

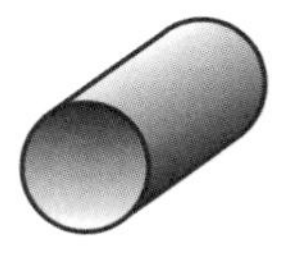

_____ circle faces

_____ curved face

36.

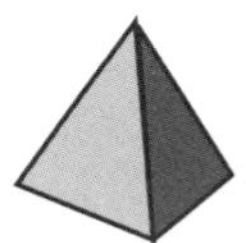

_____ square face

_____ triangle faces

/3

38. Minibuses hold 12 people. Circle how many minibuses are needed to carry 55 people.

a) 5 **b)** 4 **c)** 6 **d)** 7

/1

Answer these problems.

39. I'm thinking of a number. If I add 6 to it the answer is 21. What is my number? _______

40. I subtract 8 from a number and the answer is 14. What is my number? _______

/2

/40

acute angle	an angle smaller than a right angle, so between 0° and 90°
angle	the amount by which something turns is an angle. It is measured in degrees (°)
anticlockwise	turning in this direction
approximate	a 'rough' answer – near to the real answer
area	the area of a shape is the amount of surface that it covers
clockwise	turning in this direction
denominator	bottom number of a fraction, the number of parts it is divided into. Example: $\frac{2}{\mathbf{3}}$
difference	the difference between two numbers is the amount by which one number is greater than the other. The difference between 18 and 21 is 3
digit	there are 10 digits : 0 1 2 3 4 5 6 7 8 and 9. These make all the numbers that we use
edge	where two faces of a solid shape meet (Edge)
equivalent	two numbers or measures are equivalent if they are the same or equal
equivalent fractions	these are equal fractions. Example: $\frac{1}{2} = \frac{2}{4} = \frac{3}{6}$
estimate	is like a good guess
faces	the flat sides of a solid shape (Face)
multiple	a multiple is a number made by multiplying together two other numbers
negative number	a number less than zero on the number line.
net	the net of a 3D shape is what it looks like when it is opened out flat.
numerator	top number of a fraction. Example: $\frac{\mathbf{3}}{5}$
obtuse angle	an angle greater than a right angle but smaller than a straight line, so between 90° and 180°
polygon	any straight sided flat shape
remainder	if a number cannot be divided exactly by another number, then there is a whole number answer with an amount left over, called a remainder
rounding	rounding a whole number means to change it to the nearest ten, hundred or thousand to give an approximate number. Decimal numbers can be rounded to the nearest whole number, tenth or hundredth
sequence	a list of numbers which usually have a pattern. They are often numbers written in order
symmetrical	when two halves of a shape or pattern are identical
vertices	(single – vertex) these are the corners of 3D shapes, where edges meet (Vertex)

Progress grid

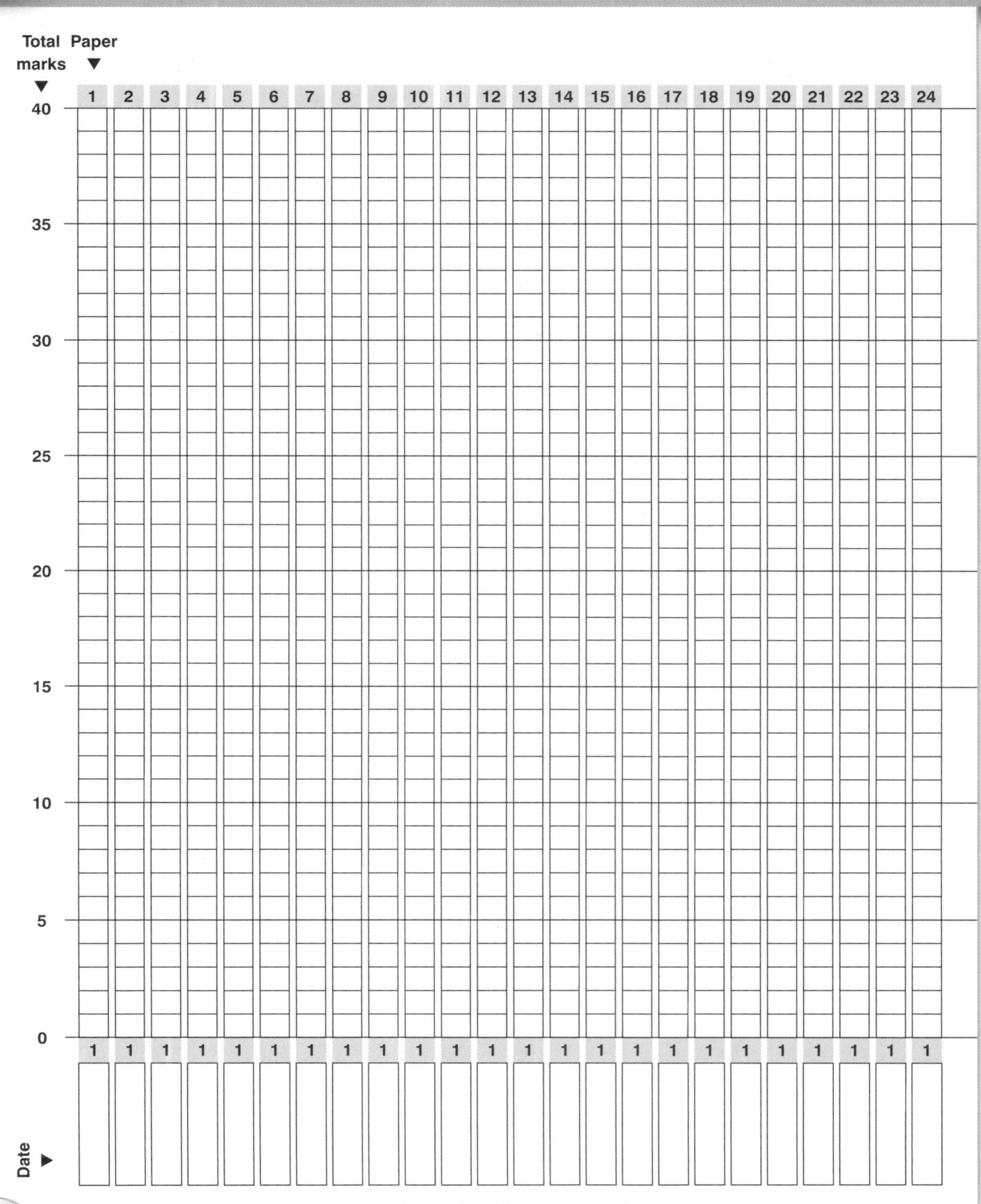

Now colour in your score!